COACHED DEVIL BY THE

IN THE SCHOOL OF ADDICTION

DUSTIN L HAWKINS

ISBN–13: 978-1-945431-18-0

Printed in the United States of America.

dustin@schoolofaddiction.org

SchoolofAddiction.org

CONTENTS

PREFACE

I've always been interested in trying to accurately describe the beautiful mind of an addict. This addiction disease is unique because it takes place in the mind, and is often linked to mental health, trauma, insecurities, and character defects. Most of the reason people use drugs and alcohol is that it makes them feel like they've finally arrived in life.

But think how valuable the one who recovers from drug and alcohol addiction is to the world? If you think about it, this entire world is being plagued by drug and alcohol addiction. There is so much to get addicted to in today's world, which is why a degree in the School of Addiction is the most important degree one can obtain. But this is a degree that can only happen inside the recovery process—because once someone recovers and turns their life around, then fellowshipping and helping others are the main ingredients to capturing long-term sobriety and true happiness.

I felt it necessary to use the Devil to write the letters to his student so that I could depict addiction and the addiction-recovery process more accurately.

The book starts out with orientation, in the same way secular schools of today have an orientation. After orientation, the reader will enter the first semester in The School of Addiction, which is where the Devil begins coaching his student through a series of persuasive letters that eventually lead the student into active addiction.

The second semester of the book is where the Devil further coaches his student through the recovery process. The reader will notice how the Devil tempts his student while at the same time creatively teaching him how to recover and become like his competitor—Jesus Christ.

Every addict knows the pull that takes place inside the mind between right and wrong, light and dark, or a devil on one shoulder and an angel on the other. Whatever way a person perceives this conflict is the right way. I think most can admit that there is some sort of positive and negative force taking up space in their mind, heart, and soul, as they battle with making right or wrong choices.

This is the second book of a three-part series and the prequel to my last book, *Coached by the Lord in the School of Addiction*. This book comes mostly from my story; however, some parts of it weave into fiction as well.

I don't write books with the intention of selling millions of copies, going on marketing tours, or whatever. I'm more interested in the creative and spiritual process of writing. I enjoy the outlet of being able to channel my thoughts into a beautiful direction, put them down on paper, and hopefully help someone who is struggling with addiction.

I've always said that addiction is a spiritual disease; my philosophy is that the solution to the spiritual disease is God. I believe that the Alcoholics Anonymous 12-Step Program—coupled with the gospel of Jesus Christ—is the true way for one to be healed of their spiritual disease. (A bold claim, I know, but that's what I believe.) I became an active member of The Church of Jesus Christ of Latter-day Saints in 2009, and it was the greatest decision of my life because it changed my life.

Throughout the second semester of the book, I use many scriptures to help describe the recovery process. I don't claim to be an expert at scriptures or even the doctrine of The Church, so please excuse me if I get some of it wrong. I'm just doing my best to show how I've used the gospel in my own life to overcome drug and alcohol addiction.

My hope is that you'll come to appreciate the creativity of this book and hopefully gain a better understanding of the disease of addiction and what it takes to recover.

Thank you for reading.

ACKNOWLEDGMENTS

To my people—the drug addicts and alcoholics—who are valiantly fighting the WAR with their addictions: Thank you for teaching me about the disease of addiction. Hopefully, this book speaks to you in a unique tone that catches your attention. You're not alone in the fight, and there's no reason at all why you can't gain your doctorate degrees in the School of Addiction and become a great asset to the world and its addiction problems.

FIGHTING THE WAR ISN'T ENOUGH IN TODAY'S WORLD.

NOW IT'S TIME TO SOAR.

ORIENTATION

Welcome to the School of Addiction, Student.

I am the Devil, sometimes called Satan or the Adversary. I am the enemy of all righteousness. I want you addicted to various substances so that you cannot follow God's plan. Oddly enough, I'm an actual spirit son of God who was once an angel "in authority in the presence of God" (D&C 76:25; see also Isaiah 14:12; D&C 76:26–27). In the premortal council in Heaven, I did not agree with God's plan of salvation. Therefore, I rebelled against God and have, ever since, sought to destroy God's earthly students in an effort to make them miserable.

You should know that the conflict between God and I was agency. I don't agree that agency is a precious gift from God. Therefore, I instead "sought to destroy the agency of man" (Moses 4:3). My exact words to God were, "I will redeem all mankind, that one soul shall not be lost, and surely I will do it; wherefore give me thine honor" (Moses 4:1).

You see, Student, I wanted the glory, I wanted to be king, and I wanted all of you to worship me without even having a choice. God wants to give you choices and opportunities to grow through your failures. I just want you to be drifting robots who have to do exactly what I say.

Because God and I failed to see eye to eye, I then persuaded "a third part of the hosts of heaven" to turn their back on God, which resulted in us being cut off from God's presence and denied the blessing of receiving a physical body, thus becoming demons and evil spirits whose sole existence is to thwart God's plan (D&C 29:36; see also Revelations 12:9).

Because of God's free agency plan, He even allows me and my team of minions to tempt you during the mortal experience (see 2 Nephi 2:11–14; D&C 29:39). My team and I seek "that all men might be miserable like unto [us]," which is why we try and lead you away from righteous living and more towards a pleasure-filled lifestyle (2 Nephi 2:27). I want nothing more than to discredit God's Plan of Happiness by distracting people from the truth. I want people addicted to drugs and alcohol; I want people addicted to pornography; I want people engulfed in selfish thoughts; and I want all of this—and much more—so that the human race will drift through life aimlessly, without ever exercising their agency. This will essentially give me what I've always wanted, which is for you to have no agency or choice, thus being slaves to me and my minions forever.

I am considered to be the father of lies, but because of God's pathetic plan of agency, you do have the option to choose my way or God's way. God's ways are slow to develop and are a bit more lasting. My ways are immediate, yet far more pleasurable. I will take you up fast, but down even faster, even like a roller coaster. And Student, roller coasters are fun. My ways are fun! God's ways are boring and full of monotony. He asks you to live simply, while I'll ask you to live fast and loud.

In the current day and age, my team and I are helping people to forget about God; it's not popular at all to speak of God and Jesus

Christ in today's world. Even in many of the world's addiction treatment centers, the 12-step repentance process is being removed, and I couldn't be happier. No system on planet Earth has caused me and my team to lose more drug-addicted followers than that of the 12-step repentance process.

In today's world, with social media and loud temptations, it has become easy for me to block people from the Holy Spirit. Now they are posting selfies and trying to promote themselves so often that they forget about working on their relationship with God. Pornography is now readily available on everyone's devices, and the Holy Spirit has no chance of dwelling inside the one who is in a relationship with pornography. Now there are mass shootings; now there are child abductions; now there are massive party scenes that create drug addicts; now there is pleasure in every form to enslave mankind. This has been "My Work and My Glory": to enslave mankind to the point where no hope and peace can be experienced by anyone.

If you think about it, today's age is my age. I am peaking! Never has there been a time in human history where vice has been so massive and prevalent. Think about how much there is to get addicted to nowadays. Addicted to energy drinks; addicted to phones, video games, and social media; addicted to drugs, alcohol, and pornography; addicted to food and the merry lifestyle; addicted to fashion and vanity; addicted to shopping and spending; addicted to gross and negative thoughts; addicted to anything and everything! If you think about it, my entire game plan is formed around addiction.

It's pretty hard to live the lifestyle of Christ in today's world, wouldn't you agree? So why fight it? "Come unto me," and go on to experience the pleasure-filled lifestyle instead.

Your Fake Friend,
The Devil

FIRST SEMESTER

MY COLLEAGUE WEED

Don't worry; I'm not addicting.

LETTER 1
THE GATEWAY

Dear Student,

You can't get physically addicted to my colleague Weed, so don't worry—just go ahead and try him. He will help you to laugh as hard as you've ever laughed. He makes everything better. He makes movies more interesting; he makes music sound better; he makes food taste better; he makes conversations more thought-provoking; he makes everything appear to be better. Weed will open up your mind to a whole new realm of heightened thinking. He will appear harmless at first, leading you to believe that a relationship with him isn't that big of a deal because, after all, Weed isn't physically addicting. He's all about the mind escape.

Weed has been called the gateway drug, and I would have to agree with mankind on some level. If you would just stick with him and only him, he will be harmless in your life—or at least he will have you believe so. His goal is to help you coast through life, carefree. His goal is to make you lazy and content with where you're at in life. He'll make you think positive thoughts quite often, and will give you interesting ideas; however, he'll make following through with those ideas a challenge. Most of the ideas that Weed will put into your mind will just remain ideas because he's not one for ambition. Weed isn't a motivator; instead, he is a laziness creator. He wants you to be a big talker, not a big doer. He will lift you in times of need but will not lead you anywhere fast.

Weed's goal is to eventually take your world over. He wants you to use him when you wake up; he wants you to use him at lunch; he wants you to use him two hours after lunch, and then two hours after that, and then two hours after that, and then two hours after that, causing your day to be filled with him until it's time to sleep. He will help you sleep and will give you good dreams. He will make you content before bedtime, leading you to mindless movies and TV shows.

Weed isn't going to bring you down to your demise like Opiate, Amphetamine, or even Alcohol will; he'll just cause you to coast. His eventual hope (and mine as well) is to assist you in furthering your relationship with the party scene since the party scene is where a new realm can be found. Weed doesn't really want you to stick with just him and him alone. Did you really believe that?

Your Fake Friend,
The Devil

LETTER 2
THE WEED SEASON

Dear Student,

I see that it's the off-season and that you have about seven months to do nothing but train for baseball's spring training that starts in March. Student, it makes me happy that you are so excited to have all of these months off to prepare physically for the upcoming season. Just relax and enjoy the off-season; I love idle time.

In the mornings, you've gotten in the habit of waking up early to take care of all of your baseball business, which includes batting practice, playing catch, and lifting weights. What are you going to do for the remainder of the day if you're always finished by noon? I have an idea for you, Student.

I realize that these first couple of weeks at home have seemed to drag for you. The morning routine just doesn't tie up enough of your day, does it? Why don't you bring some Weed into the picture to help make the remainder of the day a little better—which, I promise it will do.

I told you, Student! Weed makes the afternoon fun, right? He leads you to lunch, movies, candy, and matinees. Just relax—everything is fine—it's the off-season—you deserve it. A lot of athletes smoke Weed in the off-season, and it doesn't affect their performance, so don't worry about it—it's just a plant—and what is from the earth is of the greatest worth.

Wow! You have really come to like Weed, haven't you? What started out as smoking Weed once a day has now led to twice a day, and then three times a day, and then four times a day, eventually causing you to be high all the time, except during your morning routine. I always hoped you would use Weed in this way, but to be honest, I never really expected it. Keep using it! I actually think that it will make you a better player. You're still working hard, right? I see no harm in continued use. In fact, why don't you think about using Weed during your morning routine? Just a thought, Student.

Student, it's great that you're now buying a bag of Weed every three days. Way to be diligent. I see that you have started to stay up late playing video games and watching mindless television. There is nothing wrong with this, so keep it up. I like the fact that it's now not unusual for you to stay up until three in the morning watching TV and playing video games. Your morning routine has now started to suffer a bit, but it's okay. Who cares if it's not a morning routine anymore? Just sleep in and relax. Go ahead and move your morning routine into your afternoon routine, but do hurry through it all, so you can be done with your training and move on to the Weed escape.

I love how Weed has led you to a deep analysis of music and entertainment. You now can't wait to get high and listen to music or watch a movie. I've noticed that you rarely think about baseball anymore; it almost seems to be a burden for you now. Your workouts have become hurried and not as effective, but it's okay: you have time. You are working harder than most of the other athletes, so you're actually doing plenty to prepare for the season. Just keep enjoying the off-season routine of eating, laughing, smoking, and staying up late. It's okay that this routine has been going on for months now, and it's even more okay that spring training is slowly approaching. You'll be fine.

Yes! I've finally got you where I want you. The desire to get high and stay high has become of such importance that you are now convinced that it would be better to get high and then go do your workouts. I've been putting this concept into your head for a long time now, and finally, my deceitful work has paid off. You've heard of others getting high and being able to perform, so why can't you? Let me tell you a little secret: It's better to train high anyway. In fact, you'll be better at all things when you are high on Weed. I love where I have you. You now don't spend one waking moment of the day sober. Just relax! I think you'll like where I'm leading you.

Student, spring training is only three weeks away. Wow! Where did the time go? I see that you keep telling yourself that you're done with Weed. You even told yourself the week prior that you were done with Weed, but oddly enough, you've decided to push it back one more week. I like this game you are playing. But trust me, Student, it will be out of your system in time for a drug test anyway, so don't worry. Three weeks is plenty of time to get it out of your system, especially since you're working out so much and sweating. It's so funny how you've actually been playing this quitting game in your mind for over two months, and now you're only three weeks away from making your departure back to spring training. Your training has been going well! Don't keep worrying about getting Weed out of your system. You'll be fine; they probably won't even drug test you.

I see that you have cut way back on Weed use. You're only smoking Weed once a day now. Good job! You should be happy about the progress you've made. You seem quite confident that if you quit smoking this week, then you will be good to pass a drug test when you get to Spring Training in Florida. However, keep in mind that they probably won't even drug test you. But if they do, you'll be fine to pass because you bought one of those four-hour cleanses, which are guaranteed to work anyway, so why not just keep smoking?

Your training seems to be going well, but for some reason, you are full of fear, doubt, and insecurity concerning the future. You have noticed since you quit smoking Weed that your social interactions are a bit awkward; you feel like you can't communicate anymore. The thought of spring training scares you, doesn't it? You wonder how you're going to make it through a complete day being sober. You haven't done it in such a long time, so it seems like a hard challenge to complete a full day without taking something. I've still got you, don't I, Student?

I must admit, Student, that it's quite impressive that you have seven days of complete sobriety under your belt—well, almost seven days, if you don't count drinking. You are seven days Weed-free. Congratulations! You now feel pretty good about things, don't you? But for whatever reason, you still constantly crave an escape. This past week, you've been very irritable since quitting Weed, which has led you to have a few drinks at night—sometimes more than a few—sometimes a lot of drinks. You feel good about yourself in the sense that you are Weed-free, but at the same time, you still haven't gone a complete day without taking or drinking something. This last week, you've been telling yourself that you are going to remain sober no matter what—especially from Alcohol and Weed—which gives me another idea for you.

Nicely done, Student! You are four days away from leaving and have three days of sobriety under your belt. You can't completely say that you are happy because you're not; I won't allow it. You have noticed that for whatever reason, you can't be at peace and that you constantly want to take something in an effort to escape reality. You don't want to drink, but you can't smoke Weed either, so you decide to take a Morphine pill instead, which is all a part of my beautiful plan. I realize that you have taken them a couple of times over the past six months, but for some odd reason, you didn't seem to be that impressed with his effects. But this time, the Morphine was really enjoyable, wasn't it? He even made you happy and confident concerning the future. This time, Morphine picked you up and held you high; you felt great. Morphine is actually a good thing for you; it does no harm, because now you are content with just staying home and going to bed on time, which is perfect, because you've been stressed and worried about the upcoming season. Morphine will eliminate that stress and worry and will help you stay numb and focused.

I must say that I love how you've been taking Morphine every day until your departure. And I love even more how you've bought a few extra for the flight and first week at spring training. Nice work, and way to think ahead.

But wait, Student: How long does Morphine stay in your system?

Your Fake Friend,
The Devil

LETTER 3
STAYING THE SAME

Dear Student,

Look at you climbing the age ladder. It's been five years since getting released from the Houston Astros Organization for failing a drug test, and Weed still plays a major role in your life, as do my colleagues Opiate, Amphetamine, and Alcohol. What started off as laughs with your buddies has since turned into a way of life, and Weed has made you super content with mediocrity. The runaround for a bag and pills is still taking place; the sessions with the buddies are still taking place; the wake and bake is still taking place; the happy hour after work is still taking place; the escape from all things—such as golf, skiing, hiking, fishing, movies, and hanging out—is still taking place. Good work!

I see that depression has also crept into your life, and Weed now has a different effect on you than it did in the past. Your thoughts aren't as gratifying, and your confidence has since diminished, which is totally normal, Student. You have also become socially awkward in many ways, and your overall personality is slow. You have thought many times about quitting, but every time you do try to quit, the temptation to escape proves to be too much. It's also tough to quit because that would mean an end to hanging out with the majority of your friends. The sessions with your buddies have become an addiction in itself. The actual loading of the bowl, the rolling of the joint, or just smoking has also become an addiction, aside from actually getting high. You have found the actual process to be enjoyable, making the broad spectrum of smoking hard to get rid of. You enjoy the sessions, but you also don't enjoy the sessions. You like smoking, but you also don't like smoking. You like getting high, but you also don't like the high. In a sense, you are stuck between two worlds, and every time you try to travel to the real world, the downtime and routine change reels you back to the Weed world—back into my world.

And need I remind you, Student, that if you do choose to quit Weed, then you would have to think about quitting my colleagues Amphetamine and Opiate as well, since Weed is what helps you to come down from their heights, but also brings you up from their lows. He helps keep you out of the bars and night clubs; he helps you slow down on pills; he helps you make it through Opiate withdrawals; he helps your anxiety and depression. Weed keeps you balanced! Actually, a relationship with Weed is healthy.

At night, when you get home, you love the thought of hitting the pipe and popping a pill to then watch mindless television. You love how Weed makes TV fun and interesting. Shows that you would have never watched before are now interesting and enjoyable. Comedy Central and the Discovery Channel are now amongst your favorites. This type of entertainment is good for you, Student, so keep it up. Remember, great amounts of leisure and mindless entertainment are a good way to waste time. There is so much downtime in this life, so you must find ways to kill time, and this routine is perfect. Nice work!

I've recognized that you love going on hikes into the mountains, where you stop on occasion to smoke and reflect. Good thoughts do travel into your mind at times, but following those times, a darkness seems to creep in where you start to worry and feel regret for letting this lifestyle remain. You're constantly back and forth in your mind, wondering if certain things you did in public earlier in the day while high were weird because, in your mind, they felt weird and awkward. You seem to always be second-guessing yourself, Student, even wondering if you would have done what you did in certain social situations had you been sober. Because everything seems to be awkward, you're always thinking too deeply and over-analyzing everything you're actively involved in high.

I would say it's a good thing to be overly analytical, Student. It's a good thing to constantly be thinking about yourself. If you are always thinking about others, then how would you expect to change? Long, deep reflection with no action is a great way to be. Remember, I'm not a promoter of action or works.

It's interesting, Student, that when you are sober, you do feel okay for a time, but are always thinking about the next session, the next pill, or the next drink. What's happening to you, Student? You go a few days without pills or Weed, but those are sick days that travel slowly, and then the minute a buddy calls or you call a buddy, you are right back into the next session; back into the escape of it all. You know that you could keep this juggling act up for a little while longer, but you are also worried about your future and what it would mean to remain stuck in the same life you've been living for the past ten years. Your ambition and motivation have been stripped. If you keep this pattern up, who's to say that another 10 years won't pass you by where you'll still be standing in a circle with your buddies, smoking Weed and getting high on pills.

Your Fake Friend,

The Devil

LETTER 4
SLOW TO GET YOU

Dear Student,

Weed is the type of drug that will be slow to get you and will chip away at your character without you even realizing it. Weed isn't like Amphetamine and Opiate. Those drugs harm your character quickly, but Weed will help you remain mediocre at best. But doesn't the carefree personality lead people to feel at peace? Doesn't mediocrity mean less stress and competition? You don't need to be the best at anything, Student.

Weed will make competing in the game of life a lot harder, especially for the young adults who are amongst the middle class. The young adult who isn't involved with Weed and chooses to do all of life clear will make more progress than the one who chooses to stay in a relationship with Weed. But who is going to have the more fun time, Student? Yes, the clear student might be further along in life and standing out amongst his or her colleagues, but the clouded student will have had fun. Which is the better path to travel? I mean, look what's happened to you, Student, as a result of Weed? Look how much fun you've had.

I wonder if Weed makes it harder for people to find their way into marriage and a family? But Student, plenty of people are in a relationship with Weed and turn out to be just fine. Why does it matter if one becomes an introvert and comfortable with the routine of going home to watch mindless television and to smoke more Weed? What is the problem with being burnt out rather than being out and about being productive?

Don't you love how Weed feeds interesting conversations into the mind that often get twisted up because of how analytical you become when you are high? Oftentimes, you build out false scenarios that aren't even really about conversations, which leads to confusion and arguments about concepts that don't even matter. This is all too comical for me and my team, Student. Weed allows us to float weird ideas into your mind about spiritual matters that don't even exist. How far can I take your thoughts away from your Creator? How often can I push your thoughts away from the truth? Weed helps me to do all of this and more. Weed isn't a promoter of works, yet God is. Therefore, if you are in a relationship with Weed, you are furthering yourself from God, even though the process might be slow. But what is time anyway, Student? Again, there is nothing wrong with being ordinary and floating through this life without feeling anything. Weed will help you to coast, and there is nothing wrong with that. You don't need to be great, nor do you need to find your way into lasting relationships. The only relationship that you need to be in is with Weed.

Your Fake Friend,
The Devil

LETTER 5
EASE AND COMFORT

Dear Student,

It seems like everyone has anxiety nowadays, which gives way to the excuse to use Weed for medicinal purposes. God would have you head out your front door to go for a jog as a better way to deal with anxiety, which is a practice most people won't do since most are lazy. It's far easier, I guess, to stand in your garage and escape back into the Weed empire state of mind. But then again, you could be standing on a mountain peak to enjoy the scenery and reading instead, Student. But why would you seek to get high that way when it can come so easy through the Weed way?

But it isn't necessarily true that Weed makes you dumb, Student. At first, it will lead you to that empire state of mind, where you'll be convinced that you have all the money-making ideas only to later realize those were just dreams since Weed isn't one for ambition. They were good ideas, Student—just not ideas that you would ever put into action.

But God would say taking long walks while listening to self-help audiobooks will lead one to far better ideas than Weed ever could. Besides, Weed leads to thoughts that lead nowhere, right? And long walks and audiobooks while carrying a clear mind will lead to nostalgia, knowledge, thoughts of charity, and, finally, to action. After all, Student, the empire state of mind only leads to the clouds of forgetfulness, while sobriety leads to the solid foundation of knowledge and power.

Some of this may be true, but much is false. The common theme that I will be weaving in and out of your mind is one of leisure and works. How much work are you willing to put in to capture the rewards of God? His highs are linked to works, Student. The ways of Weed are linked to laziness and only talking about your big dreams.

On Weed, it's hard to get anything done because you will constantly be losing things like misplacing your wallet back in the house after you've already gone to the store. And then it seems so hard to drive back to your house for your wallet, and by that time you've come up with an excuse as to why you didn't need to go to the store anyway. This is so funny to me, Student. What a waste of time!

Wouldn't you agree that it's just easier to not do anything while on Weed? The career man, like yourself, might lean on Weed at work to get things done, but when he heads home to participate in the work inside his family—which God would say is the most important work—he is far too burned out and only wants to smoke Weed again so that he can slow down, watch TV, play some video games, and not be stressed from how hard his workday was.

God would promote that this same man stay sober all day and come home without wearing the stress of work on his sleeve so that he could be his best self as he now goes to work for his family. Now, he is taking them out to be active on a summer night in an effort to create new family memories they all can lean on in the years to come. He might even be leading his entire family in prayer before bed. Then, in the morning, he gets up to do it all over again.

But Student, do you really believe that the greatest work one can do inside the human experience is the work inside the family? I would say that always escaping your stress will help you to be a better father inside your family. Selfishness will always exist anyway, Student, regardless if you are sober or not. You can still give of your time and talents to your children if you are high. Maybe you will be a little more selfish if you are in a relationship with Weed because it's just one more relationship you will have to juggle. But to think less of yourself and more of your kids seems ridiculous. If you can't take care of yourself, how will you take care of your family? Weed will help you to think about yourself often, which won't be a bad thing.

I think it all depends on who you want to be in this life, Student. A great many are getting by fine using Weed to cope with stress and anxiety. But is that who you really want to be, Student? One who can't cope with stress? How will you ever expect to learn and grow if you don't deal with stress? Then, after using Weed consistently for seven-plus years, you might realize that you've watched just a little too much TV, played far too many video games, and eaten way too much junk food.

But hey, at least you will be free from stress and anxiety.

Your Fake Friend,

The Devil

UNIT 2

THE PARTY
SCENE

A little partying never hurt anybody.

LETTER 6
A NIGHT IN THE SCENE

Dear Student,

I love how you're out all night, partying, drinking, smoking, laughing, and enjoying yourself. This night is never going to end—look, it's only 10 p.m. The night is still young. Don't you love how you feel right now, Student? Nothing seems to matter. Why don't you go back outside and smoke another cigarette; then, when you go back inside, have another drink. Maybe have a mixed drink or a shot this time instead of a beer.

Now that you are buzzed and feeling great, maybe it's time to smoke some Weed. There is nothing better than being a little drunk and then smoking some Weed. The laughs are insanely fun—the combination will put you on another level of happiness.

Don't forget that you have a whole pack of cigarettes as well. Don't you love chain-smoking cigarettes when you are partying like this? They also bring their own unique head change to the night. Each and every time you go out to smoke one, you're enlightened. Cigarettes are great for nights like this. They add so much more to the experience.

Soon, it will be midnight. It's still early, so don't worry, Student. You can shut it down around two in the morning. You can start drinking water in the next hour or so. But don't you want to go further and feel better? Why don't you go out and have another cigarette and then rally the troops to smoke Weed again? I'm sure they will all think it's a good idea. Another shot sounds good also, doesn't it? You don't seem to be that drunk, so maybe another shot will make you feel even better. In fact, why don't you just go take another shot right now while you're thinking about it?

Now it's two in the morning. It's late . . . but not that late. You don't do this very often, so it's okay. At three in the morning, you can start drinking water and looking for a ride home. You don't want this night to end, do you? It has to end sometime. Tomorrow's going to be rough.

How are you going to get through it? Actually, don't worry about it, what's done is done. You can worry about tomorrow … tomorrow. Why don't you have a few more beers? Just have two more beers and then shut it down at 3 p.m. and start drinking water.

Oh wow! How did it get to be 4 p.m., and how are you going to get home? Why did you do this? Student, forget tomorrow; the entire next week is going to be rough. Why can't you just quit doing this? Aren't you tired of living this on-and-off lifestyle where you're happy one minute and sad the next? What are you going to do about tomorrow? How are you going to make it through? You are going to be so depressed and down. Why can't you just be normal? Don't you hate drinking and partying like this? It's comical to see you keep relapsing. Go ahead and tell yourself that you are never doing this again, like you've done so many times in the past. I get it—you hate Alcohol, and it makes you feel horrible—so why do you keep doing it?

So now, what's your plan to deal with today's depression and pounding headache? What can you take to make your headache go away? Oh, I know what you can take: my friend Opiate.

Your Fake Friend,
The Devil

LETTER 7
A WEEK IN THE SCENE

Dear Student,

In the beginning, the scene was good to you, right? You laughed and made all kinds of new friends; you've been living life to the fullest, even experiencing pleasure at the highest level. Let's face it: For some time now, you've been deeply interested in cutting loose often to have a few drinks and smoke cigarettes. That works until you wake up Monday morning feeling like you were hit by a train—right in time to jump back into work and real life.

Monday becomes a hazy day filled with negativity, heartburn, and headaches. You are definitely not at your best, but it's okay. Just get through the day—it's almost time for Monday Night Football, and your favorite team is playing. You kept telling yourself that you were only going to have a few beers, but you ended up having eight. It's okay! Keep laughing, cheering, eating, and drinking, and smoke a few more cigarettes along with some Weed. Then you can be on your way home.

Well, it's now Tuesday morning, Student. You don't feel that bad, do you? It's totally normal to be feeling negative and lethargic as you start the day. No one is happy in the mornings anyway. I realize that everything is bothering you, so why don't you find some way to take the edge off? The next party scene is on Thursday night—the 49ers and the Vikings are playing, and you love the 49ers, so you at least have that to look forward to. Just get through today and Wednesday by leaning on Weed. Then Thursday will end up being just like Monday: laughing, cheering, eating, and smoking.

Congratulations, Student: you made it to Friday. Nice work! It's time to relax and get ready for that party at your buddy's house where you can have some more laughs, drinks, smokes, more drinks, more smokes, and of course, smoke a ton of Weed. I'm excited!

Just relax, Student, and realize that today (Saturday) is going to be a huge hangover blur, but just go ahead and sleep all day; you don't have to do anything. All you need to do is get refreshed and ready for Sunday night, right? And then the entire week will repeat itself just like it's been doing for years now. Isn't this the abundant way of life, Student?

Your Fake Friend,

The Devil

LETTER 8
THE SCENE GRAB

Dear Student,

The party scene has grabbed hold of you, hasn't it? You've been loving the laughter, the escape, the girls, the drinking, and the loss of inhibition. However, you've gotten into a little bit of trouble lately because of the scene. You've just gotten your second DUI, this time in possession of Weed. I see that you are starting to feel remorseful and mad at yourself and the scene. I never promised there would be no consequences inside this style of life. Principles of truth are principles of truth that don't change, and if you make a series of incorrect choices over a long period of time, you are bound to experience some negative consequences along the way. However, don't let these negative consequences get you down. If you go too far down, you might actually start thinking about changing. I'm actually not a fan of rock bottom. I would rather you hover just above ground.

I hear you keep saying that you are going to quit the scene for good, but it's just not quite that easy, Student, since your relationship with the scene is strong. You've been doing pretty well for the last little while, but New Year's Eve is right around the corner, and your buddy is having a party. You can't miss that party, right? Everyone parties on New Year's Eve. It's okay to let loose, and you've been doing so good.

New Year's was great to you, wasn't it? The scene gave you everything you wanted and more. You partied, you smoked, you drank, you laughed, you smoked some more, and most importantly, you tried something new. You did your first line of Cocaine, and you liked it. In fact, you loved it, and I couldn't be happier.

Now that you've tried something new that you like, it becomes a powerful new reward in your mind. So powerful that the following weekend you are ready to party again. Have you already forgotten the trouble that the scene has caused you in the past?

Now you are doing Cocaine on the weekends pretty consistently, along with Alcohol and the rest of the party scene. Doesn't it feel good to be back in a relationship with the scene? I realize that on the days that follow, you are feeling depressed and low, and you can't seem to find happiness at all. And for no reason at all, anxiety has started to creep into your life. Here's an idea: Why don't you get into a serious relationship with Opiates? You have obviously dabbled in the past, but never have you taken an interest in my best friend, Roxy. She will make all of your feelings of stress and anxiety dissipate and make you feel happy, calm, and content.

You see, I told you that Roxy is an amazing friend. With her now coming on to the scene, everything slowly starts to change, which is what you wanted anyway. You're staying somewhat connected to the party scene, but slowly the scene is shifting to one that is more secluded, isolated, and dark.

The weekends have completely changed for you, haven't they, Student? Sitting home on Friday and Saturday nights really isn't that big of a deal anymore. You actually seem to be in a better position since getting into a relationship with Roxy. You're staying home, aren't out drinking anymore, and are content to do so. This means you are making progress, and your anxiety and stress levels can be managed by Roxy. You don't have to worry about your law troubles anymore. Just sit back and let Roxy work for you.

There is no turning back now—you've gone too far—which is why, in closing, I feel I can share a few secrets with you. Here goes: Roxy is slowly stealing away your free agency. She won't tell you about the troubles that are associated with her dark world. She won't tell you that you will become less confident in yourself and that your self-esteem will slowly diminish into nothing. She won't tell you about the financial crisis she is leading you and your family toward. She won't tell you about the relationships that will be damaged and the trust issues that will incur. She won't tell you about the loss of friendships and hobbies. She won't tell you about the negative outlook on life that creeps in. She won't tell you that her plan is to slowly lead you to jail or death.

Your Fake Friend,
The Devil

LETTER 9
THE SCENE PATHS

Dear Student,

The father who stays home on a Friday night to spend time with his family while remaining sober has a far different experience than you, Student. You go out every Friday night, get drunk and high through my party scene, only to then come home in the middle of the night after your family is already in bed. The next morning for you proves to be challenging when the kids wake up early and want to play. Now, due to your lack of sleep and being sick, you aren't able to be your best self. This progresses to a routine of weekend after weekend and night after night of you valuing the party scene more than your family. Student, your family thinks this is just who you are, so don't worry about it. They will never know of the great man that lies behind the now selfish man.

Think how boring life would be if you weren't selfish, Student. Think if you were the type of man who came home night after night being his so-called best self because he is his sober self. This type of man actually stays home on Friday and Saturday nights to spend time with his family around the dinner table and watch movies. At the close of the night, he tells his kids stories and tucks them in tightly and thanks God in his own personal prayers for the blessings that he and his family have received. This man even spends time with his wife, where he communicates with her, and they become even closer friends. And when the morning arrives and the kids are awake, this man hops out of bed and is ready to play and make his family breakfast. He chases the kids around the house, playing with them, laughing with them, wrestling with them, teaching them, and, most importantly, Student, getting to know them.

But Student, it's obvious you are far from this latter man. I paint this picture for you now not to motivate you, but to discourage you. The road is long and hard, Student. Good luck trying to become this man. And why would you want to become such a man when boredom becomes the result? Trust me, it will be far easier to stay in hiding. You have lived this way for far too long, and to change your habits now would nearly be impossible.

Your Fake Friend,
The Devil

UNIT 3

MY COLLEAGUE OPIATE

I, Opiate, am the religion of the people.

LETTER 10
THE BACK PAIN

Dear Student,

Since hurting your back during your last season of professional baseball, the pain has become very burdensome, even unbearable, and has continued to get worse as the years have progressed. Your left leg constantly throbs, and intense shooting nerve pain travels all the way down to the base of your foot. You must be miserable.

Student, keep going to your family doctor for refills of Percocet 10s to help you with the pain. You need them to help you deal with the physical pain as well as the emotional pain and stress that accompanies everyday living. Just think about how much better you feel when you take them during family events, movies, dinners, or any other event.

I'm sorry that back surgery is needed. During this past year, your leg pain has become unbearable; you even walk with a limp. Student, you need this surgery, so just accept it. The surgery will be a great thing for you. Not only will your leg and back get better, but you will also have another excuse to keep using my good friend Percocet.

The surgery went well, and your pain seems to have gone away, although you would never know it because of how much medication you are on. I love how you have convinced yourself that you are constantly in pain and that more pain medication is needed. You have built up a great tolerance to my friend Percocet, which is a good thing. Now you will be led into a relationship with my even better, more effective friend, Roxicontin. Even the doctor has said that you are going to have back pain for the rest of your life, which gives you an entire lifetime to spend with Opiate. This is great news, Student.

I see that the pain clinic has put you on four Roxys a day, which means you can take 28 pills a week. Remember, you have to take these pills because you are in pain, and they will help you, regardless of their negative effects and consequences. The mood swings and negative aura that constantly follow you around are just a few of the side effects of being on Roxy. Everyone knows you have a hurt back, anyway, so just keep using that as an excuse to always be unhappy.

I realize that your prescription timeline is now all out of whack. The pills are running out about 10 days before they are supposed to, but don't let this bother you. You know friends and family members who have them, right? Your sister just had a baby. A C-section, right? Go and pretend to visit Mom and Baby, and when the time is right, go through the medicine cabinet and make the score.

Wow, Student! It's been three years since the surgery, and you are in a dark cycle of prescription refills, running out of your prescription early, hustling to find pills during the time between your next refill, stealing pills, spending money you don't have, stealing money, dishonesty, loss of integrity, job loss, relationship problems, unhappiness, and negativity. You are unhealthy spiritually, emotionally, and physically. You have zero respect from anyone anymore. Everyone knows what road you've gone down, but you're too blinded by my friend Opiate to even realize the person you have become. Just remember, Student: It's all okay because you have a bad back. Keep being full of self-pity; you have more problems than everyone else. You are special, Student.

Your Fake Friend,
The Devil

LETTER 11
THE CRAVING

Dear Student,

I offer you a craving. Something intense is going to happen inside your mind that will cause you to crave my colleague Opiate. The thought, at first, will start small and far away, but then slowly, yet quickly, it will travel down into the details of your past memories of Opiate use. Isn't it interesting how time automatically slows down when these cravings happen? Now you start looking at the clock, and if you have any sort of appointment, meeting, family event, or anything where you must be social, then you want Opiate to help make whatever it is that's coming up to be better, more fun, and more enjoyable. Now you are calling to get Opiate because, in your mind, you have already seen yourself at that social gathering being lifted on him. Going without him makes you hurt inside and doesn't even seem possible. If it's a work meeting, then you feel as if you cannot even step in the door without Opiate in your system. And this now goes for everything. The Opiate fix has to happen because it doesn't seem realistic for it not to happen anymore. Therefore, you make aggressive phone calls in an effort to capture what you feel must happen.

Aggressive actions also take place, such as stealing, manipulating, and searching. If you do make the call, and the score is going to happen, but for whatever reason, you have to wait a few hours to pick up, well, this hurts even more. Remember, time has now slowed down since the craving occurred. And anyway, the social gathering is in an hour, so two hours is not acceptable, so you'll just have to show up late or even miss your meeting, which obviously means excuses and lying are now a must.

I guess you still have the option of making a phone call, going on a hike, going to an AA meeting, or even participating in prayer and scripture study, though you must be courageous enough to go and participate in such experiences even when you don't feel like it. Do you have this sort of courage at this very moment, Student? Most times, you have failed, but other times you have succeeded. What's it going to be this time? Every time you have had the courage to go and create an experience that involves scenery, an elevated heart rate, and praying to God, you have beat my cravings 100 percent of the time. However, you have failed in the past when you decided not to compete against me by instead choosing the easy reward over the hard reward. Need I remind you that my rewards are easy and fast—but do not last. Yet God's rewards are hard and slow—but inexhaustible.

But you seem to like the chase and runaround, don't you? The process and chaos of it all are attractive in some weird way, right? You know that it's wrong and where it will lead you, but for some odd reason, you are attracted to the chaos and pain of it all.

Keep in the front of your mind how glorious it would be to have Opiate in your system and pocket. Such thoughts are then linked to past memories of having them in your system and pocket. And on and on this fairy tale will go, my friend. Don't try and fight it by replacing it with some sort of health system. Health isn't my friend. After all, why would I want you feeling better about yourself? Why would I want you progressing and moving upwards in life? Just relax and stay on pause. There is absolutely no reason at all for you to do anything with your life.

Your Fake Friend,
The Devil

LETTER 12
THE DOCTOR'S OFFICE

Dear Student,

My craving worked! You had that little bit of back pain this morning, but if you are being completely honest, it never amounted to much. It was during your drive to work that this back pain created a tiny thought about my friend Percocet and how, in the past, he made you feel so warm and comfortable during your back surgeries. It's interesting how you knew—but chose to ignore—that if you allowed this tiny thought to travel forward anymore, it would lead you to a place that you have since put behind you, which is the doctor's office in search of Opiate.

Now you start envisioning what it would be like to get Percocet and how it would not only make your back pain go away, but also the mood enhancement it would lead you to having, which would make work a whole lot more fun, knowing you had pills in your pocket to burn through that could help you to be more proactive and talkative. Now your heart rate goes up, and the thought of going to work without them in your pocket does not even seem doable. Your back pain is now secondary because, in all reality, the back pain never amounted to much, but it triggered the warm thought of using them to be more social, proactive, and productive. Just think: You can also use them at night to help you live in the moment with your wife and kids. They like you better anyway when you are on them.

On the flip side, Student, what you are about to do is wrong and could lead you down a dark path. But those thoughts of euphoria, for whatever reason, seem to far outshine this simple thought of staying sober and doing the right thing.

Now you have a huge tug of WAR taking place in your mind as you sit outside the doctor's office, debating on whether to go in or not, and I couldn't be happier. I love seeing you wrestle with right and wrong. I'm on one shoulder, and God is on the other. Which side will you choose, Student? Go ahead and think about calling someone to see if they can talk you out of it, but you don't really want anyone to talk you out of it anyway. What's the point? Go ahead and leave and drive around for a minute in the hope that leaving might help you to change your mind, but this only leads you to call your work to make up an excuse as to why you are going to be late. Nice work, Student! You finally made up your mind, and there is no turning back now. Just think about it: There is no way you can go to work without Opiate. In your mind, you've already seen and felt what it would be like to be on him at work and how much more fun and enjoyable he will make work. Student, people will actually like you more because of how proactive and happy you will be, which is why you must be in a relationship with Opiate today!

Just relax as you sit here inside the doctor's office. You should actually be excited. It's not going be hard to convince the doctor of your need for Opiates because of your past history with back surgery. Don't let the shameful, sad feelings bother you. Remember, you do need the pills for your back pain. Keep telling yourself that you are in a great amount of pain, and soon enough, you will actually believe it to be true. Then you won't be lying at all. Yes, I realize that, in all truthfulness, you just want the pills to escape the pressures of life, but it feels more ethical to lean on the back excuse. That's what the doctor wants to hear, anyway.

Wow, that performance you put on for the doctor was impressive! Your best yet. You even cried a little; you're a great actor, my friend. Now you can head off to work to make the vision you've been having about the workday come true.

However, Student, I must give you some hard advice. The vision you've been chasing after can't come true because it was actually comprised of old memories you were chasing. No matter how fast you take those pills in an effort to capture the ultimate high, it will only lead to increased sadness, irritability, and regret. When you're all out, you will be left feeling empty and sick, but for some reason, you will still be chasing those old memories of past use, which will lead you back to the doctor's office time and time again to get a refill. You see, you've now opened the patient-doctor relationship door, which means you can go back and see her in a month to get more pills. There will be no more drug dealers; just hopping around to different doctors, which will be a good thing, Student, because getting them from a doctor isn't illegal.

Your Fake Friend,

The Devil

LETTER 13
THE OPIATE RUT

Dear Student,

I can see that you're in a rut, which makes me happy. Your ways these past few weeks have turned dark. Your path before these dark weeks had been a path of lightness, which I did not like at all. I can see the pattern of your addiction, and this causes me to question who you really are. Who are you, Student? For weeks, you'll walk the light path with charity and brightness in your heart. These weeks you seem to be happiest, though it's still not enough, is it? Student, you never seem to be happy or content, even when you're sober. It seems as if you always want more, even when you have as much as you need. Why is this the case with you, Student? Aren't you tired of going back and forth from light to dark and dark to light? This routine has to be exhausting for you. Why don't you just quit God's ways altogether and come my way? My way is the easy way, Student! You won't have to try anymore. You won't have to work on yourself as much. You won't need to read your scriptures, attend church, or help people anymore. You won't have to be reading about Christ or praying anymore. And anyway, Student, my substances will actually help you to be a better father and husband, which means your example to your children will be automatic instead of forced.

I play possum with all of my clients, Student, but I especially play it with you. I see how bad you want to be rid of my addictive substances. I also see how hard you work to stay on God's path. My work is more rewarding when I cause you to fall away, which is why I often lay low for a time and just wait for the perfect opportunity to strike.

That one particular day a few weeks back when I put the idea in your mind to take a few Percocets for back pain has slowly led you into my shadows once again. I had you convinced that it was no big deal and that you needed them for a little back soreness. What started out with plans of only taking two eventually led to taking eight in a single night's time. You tried to only take two that night, but you loved the heightened attitude Opiate provided, so you ended up chasing that feeling for the remainder of the night, which, in the end, proved to be a total letdown and failure. You should know better by now that this chase never amounts to anything but irritability, heartache, and depression. Even I was impressed with how far you went that night. You had been doing so well in the months previous, and I was not expecting that kind of intensity. It just goes to show that my substancces are powerful, and no matter how long you go without, their grips are embedded deep within your mind.

It's interesting how you are quick to forget about the irritability and negativity that accompanies Opiate use. You also seem to be quick to forget about the so-called beautiful ways of God, which is why you keep coming back down my path. I'm so glad that you are quick to forget, because if you weren't, then my game wouldn't exist. And since my game is temporary pleasure, the memory proves to be a powerful tool for me and my team in leading you back time and time again.

Student, are you going to be able to get out of my rut this time? You have succeeded many times in the past, but maybe this time is different. Maybe this time you'll just quit and forever come my way. I realize that the power of God is great and that His way does bring lasting peace if you can endure. But can you endure long enough? That is the question. His ways are slow to develop; my ways are quick and immediate. My ways will push your problems aside, helping you to coast through life. His ways will bring your problems towards you with hopes that a learning experience will take form. He thinks that by you dealing with adversity through a clear lens, you will actually learn and progress as a human being. I guess that makes sense to a point, but why not take the edge off while learning at the same time? You don't need to be sober all of the time to learn, Student. Let Opiate help you to overcome your weaknesses and fears. Opiate will give you a great amount of courage, and there has to be a learning experience in that, right?

The decision is yours, Student. You do have the freedom to choose, because that was God's plan from the beginning, not mine. If it had been up to me, you would have had no choice but to follow after me. I don't like free agency, which is why I'm so adamant about using Opiate to steal your free agency. I want you to be trapped by Opiate; I want you to get sick when you don't have Opiate; I want you to steal for Opiate; I want you to get in trouble because of Opiate; I want you to go to jail because of Opiate; I want to steal all of your free agency through the use of Opiate. Again, free agency was not my plan, and because of my prideful ways, I'm still looking to make my plan come to pass. What better way for me to succeed than through the use of my best friend, Opiate?

Your Fake Friend,
The Devil

LETTER 14
THE OPIATE RELAPSE

Dear Student,

You don't want to make the call for Opiate, but you do want to make the call for Opiate. You've been pathetically begging God for help in overcoming this craving for Opiates. I understand your worry, Student, but don't let the idea of not becoming the best version of yourself trouble you. Remember, you are a better person on Opiates, anyway.

I realize that the last few weeks of sitting inside this Opiate rut have been hard on you. But hey, at least you are still trying to exercise and eat healthily. However, your thoughts are on Opiate the most, which is a big deal for me and my team. You see, we almost lost you a while back, but how silly of us to think such foolish thoughts.

We've now got you to the point of thinking about Opiate all of the time. Even when you have him in your system, you're still thinking about how you can get more of him. And when you are without him, you crave him, and you will go to great lengths to get more of him. And when you are having conversations with friends and family, you aren't even listening to what's being said, because all you now think about is how and when you can get Opiates back into your system.

It's interesting how you are now snorting these Opiate pills, which is something you've never done before. The snort delivery has made an impact on your mind, Student. A new reward, right? This is dangerous territory, my friend. You can't keep this up, can you, Student? You know that your character isn't growing in the right direction, which is stressful. Instead of your character growing in a bright way, it's now slowly growing in a dark way. More and more, you find yourself having the manipulative and selfish mind frame that bends and twists every situation in an effort to flood your pleasure and reward center. Even just a few weeks ago, you were getting high through God's spiritual system of health. Oh, how fast things can change, Student.

The Opiate reward is a challenging one to escape once you open his door. But now, with Opiate in your system, you feel free inside your mind and can now experience life to the fullest. You love the thought of taking Opiate and then anticipating the warm feeling that comes just twenty minutes after ingestion. You can't wait for the better mood to come forth, can you? You can't wait to share in beautiful conversations with your family members and friends. Most of the time without Opiate in your system, you stay inside your head and feel anxiety if you have to talk to people. But with Opiate in your system, you are a master communicator, and people seem to love you.

Procrastination has always been a big problem in your life, Student. But guess what? No such procrastination exists now that you're back in a relationship with Opiate. Now, you have the ability to get things done, which is exciting and fun. Returning phone calls now becomes fun;

sending out emails now becomes fun; spending time at home with your wife and kids now becomes fun. All things become more enjoyable in a small window of time. But then that fun window closes. The memory of that window, however, doesn't, prompting the chase for that window again. You chase a memory, Student, and then when you snort another Opiate pill, that window doesn't last nearly as long as the first window, nor does it look the same. It is far dimmer. Each and every time this cycle repeats itself, that window shuts quicker and quicker, and gets dimmer and dimmer, until finally there is no open window at all—just a glass pane that is dark and black giving you no opportunity to see the beauty of the world. Instead of once having a window, you are now behind the bars of Opiate, where you are physically, psychologically, and emotionally trapped by him. No more highs take place, but only maintenance in an effort to not get sick.

I'm sorry that you are back in the Opiate prison, Student. Good luck finding your way out this time.

Your Fake Friend,

The Devil

MY COLLEAGUE
AMPHETAMINE

You need me so that you can be productive and happy.
I make you limitless.

LETTER 15
THE AMPHETAMINE SALT

Dear Student,

I see that you are starting to feel pressure to perform, so let me introduce you to my good friend Ephedrine. She will treat you right! She will give you the increase in energy and positive outlook you need at this time in your life. You will love how she will make you feel. You'll start waking up with her, you'll start using her to curb your appetite, and, most importantly, you'll start using her whenever you need to be more productive.

Go ahead and keep using her on a daily basis to be productive and active. Go to the gym with her; play games with her; go to work on her; study with her; use her to do everything that requires physical activity or even effort, Student. Don't you feel better with her in your pocket and system at all times?

I see that Ephedrine's effectiveness is wearing thin and that she cannot perform like she once used to. That's where I step in and introduce you to my even better friend, Amphetamine. She will give you everything Ephedrine could and more. She will give you the most euphoric breath of life you've ever experienced, leading you to believe that you can accomplish anything. She will make you intensely proactive for a time; she will make you social and talkative for a time; she will give you confidence at work for a time; she will give you confidence at school for a time; she will make writing papers fun and enjoyable for a time; she will make work fun and enjoyable for a time; she will make paying bills fun and enjoyable for a time. You will love what she has to offer . . . for a time.

But remember, fun can't last forever. And when it ends, she is going to drop you into the deepest, darkest hole imaginable. She is going to make you want more of her, and when you do get more of her, you will still want even more of her because she loves to be chased. She feels special when she's chased.

When you've used Amphetamine to the fullest throughout your day, she will then make you crave relief from my other friend and colleague Opiate. He will lift you out of the dark hole she has dropped you in, show you a good time, and drop you in one of his own. Then, you will need Amphetamine again to climb out of Opiate's hole. And the cycle will repeat.

Your Fake Friend,
The Devil

LETTER 16
THE STUDENT

Dear Student,

Look how my friend Amphetamine has given you the energy and confidence to go back to school and get your MBA even though you are working full time and have a family. Again, what a blessing Amphetamine has been in your life.

I'm glad to see that you are on the same great system of snorting two Adderall and then working on a research paper. Don't you feel amazing right now? Is there any other place in the world you'd rather be than sitting here with a full bottle of Adderall by your side? How fun is this? You can just sit here for hours, get high, and write a research paper. And the great thing about all of this is that you are going to get a high-level degree that will lead you to excel in life. Rest assured, Student: You are on the right track.

Isn't it awesome how two hours have gone by seamlessly? The work is still somewhat fun, right? Just let your phone ring and stay focused on the paper; you don't need to be interrupted. However, Student, I must remind you that the comedown is near. You don't want to come down.

You need to keep working. In order to not come down, you need to snort two more Adderall.

Student! Before we proceed to the next bump, isn't it interesting how just the thought of the euphoric escape that awaits you makes the current comedown you are experiencing immediately go away? In a sense, you are already euphoric and happy even though you haven't taken your next bump of Adderall. It's so great that you have a full bottle right by your side. It's so comforting, isn't it? This anticipation floods your endorphins and leaves you with an early high. Remarkable!

Now you are off and rolling with your next bump. Go ahead and allow this cycle to repeat itself a few more times: euphoria, starting to come down, force-eat some food, more pills, euphoria. But haven't you noticed that the window of euphoria keeps getting smaller and smaller, and the comedown starts sooner and sooner? Before long, there will be no euphoric feeling—just a zing, a comedown, and then it will be time to take Opiates.

Your Fake Friend,
The Devil

LETTER 17
THE SALESMAN

Dear Student,

You now have children, a wife, and a mortgage. Money is tight due to the Great Recession. I see that you are doing the best you can as a father, but the party scene, coupled with responsibility, has caused you to sink into depression. Your nights and days have become full of ups and downs, and the downs last much longer.

Here! Keep taking this Adderall, Student. He will help pull you out of this depressive funk and will get you motivated once again. After all, they call him the "happy pill" because he will make you happy and euphoric concerning the future. And guess what? Adderall works even better if you snort him, as you already know.

Isn't it amazing how proactive and productive Adderall has made you? I can tell that you now love sitting at your computer when he starts to kick in. You feel like he locks you into the day from the get-go. Your planning for the day has become more focused, and you seem to be more confident when setting appointments and making calls for your sales job. I told you that my friend Adderall would be a good drug for you. And guess what? You need it anyway because you have ADHD, which makes him perfectly fine to be using.

How great is it that, after you get your sales day lined up through the phone, you can now go meet with people while being in an Adderall-induced euphoric mindset. He leads you to feeling so happy and excited about having conversations with people.

I see that the Adderall has started to wear thin in your system, and you can feel his effects tapering. Remember, you have a 1:30 p.m. appointment, so go ahead and snort two more Addis around 1 so they kick in at the perfect time during your appointment. Don't worry! Adderall won't let you down! He will lead you back into those same euphoric feelings so you can put on your top performance during this meeting.

Student, you killed that appointment! Nice work! Just a reminder that your next appointment is at 4:30 p.m., so you have some time to relax since it's only 3. I realize that you are not hungry at all, but maybe you should force some food down so you can feel good about snorting two more Addis at 4 p.m. Health is wealth, right? I don't really care if you eat or not, but I think you will feel better about my plans for the remainder of the day if you do eat something. I need you feeling confident and proactive going into that 4:30 meeting so that we can keep this system of health going. Just ignore your current sweaty, uncomfortable situation, and go ahead and choke down the food so you can then put more Adderall back into your system.

I'm sorry that your 4:30 p.m. appointment didn't go as well as your 1:30 meeting. I've made mention in the past concerning the side effects of Adderall. He will take you up quickly, but after continued use, you will only be chasing normal. Your memory will always remind you of how great the first dose was, but you will never capture the same euphoric feeling as you did during the first experience.

Now it's 5 p.m., and you don't feel well in your mind at all. It's okay that you don't want the day to end. It doesn't have to, Student. Just keep working so you can take more Addis in the hope of feeling good again. Doesn't the thought of going an entire sleepless night without taking Addis bother you? Maybe go eat again, and then around 6:30 p.m., you can snort your final two Addis for the day.

Student! How are you going to sleep tonight? How are you going to feel better going into the nighttime experience? You feel absolutely horrible, don't you? I'm sorry for how dark your thinking is and how there seems to be no hope for the future. Who needs hope anyway? What about taking my friend Opiate to help you with this Adderall comedown? How can you get some pain pills? What if you went to your mom's or grandparents' to get some? You can tell them you hurt your back. You can manipulate them into giving you some just like you have done in the past.

Oh, what a relief it is that you scored sixty Percocet 10s from your grandma. Student, have I told you how good of an actor you are? Don't you feel so much better about things? Your brain is back to a state of equilibrium. The Percocet actually lifted you similarly to the Adderall, only in a more relaxed, sedated way. Look how happy you are and how good you are feeling. You should be even happier about the fact that you have 57 left.

Your Fake Friend,

The Devil

LETTER 18
THE RELAPSE

Dear Student,

Your memory proves to be all too powerful. The thought of that euphoric escape clouds all judgment to the point where all reasonable thinking leaves your mind. No matter how hard you have been working at living the lifestyle of Christ, my team and I will always find a way to intervene. I'll use your memory against you, Student. I'll provide vivid flashbacks of that once-euphoric state of mind that you used to visit so frequently. I will cause, through your memory, a natural happiness flush to take place in your mind, making it so you are high even prior to taking Amphetamine. You can see that Amphetamine is at your fingertips; therefore, I'll help you create a scenario in your head that almost makes you feel like you've already obtained him.

As the scenario continues to unfold in your mind, the natural happiness flush occurs. You are, in a sense, already high from Amphetamine because, in your mind, you are going to take the pills no matter what. Nothing is going to stop you, not even embarrassment. Your mind is made up, and the memorable euphoric thinking is back in your mind, clearer than ever before, and you can't wait for the Amphetamine experience.

Once you get it, you feel regretful and embarrassed about the runaround and chase that took place to obtain it. But I will not let you stop, Student. You have a routine planned out, remember? A routine of how you're going to use Amphetamine—a very memorable routine—is all part of your well-thought-out game plan. This is a game plan that has been ingrained in your mind from past use and is methodically formulating once again.

Once the pill is down the hatch, you cannot wait for it to kick in. When it first kicks, you want to be in the place you had pictured in your mind so you can enjoy that first twenty minutes of euphoria to the fullest.

I don't blame you. You want to feel productive and organized. Maybe you should make a quick phone call and have a good positive conversation. It would be a good experience to talk with someone about something real, because that euphoric feeling will magnify your communication skills, allowing the conversation to move in a magical direction.

After the thirty minutes is up, you know it's all downhill from here, Student—unless, of course, you can find some more. I don't think you can, however, because of the awkward relationships you have since created—and possibly damaged—through the initial chase. So now what's next, Student? You and I both know what's next: THE COMEDOWN.

The comedown from Amphetamine starts to creep closer, and it starts to hurt. It hurts so bad in your mind that you are convinced that you need Opiate. Only Opiate has the power to help you stop hurting.

The chase is now on for Opiate, and nothing's going to stop you from obtaining him. Just as with the Amphetamine memory, the Opiate memory to cure the Amphetamine comedown also becomes clear. I have led you to use Opiate in the past to come down off of Amphetamine, so I now use that same Opiate help memory. The memory of Opiate is so powerful that all reason and logic leave your thinking entirely. You will stop at nothing—won't you, Student? You will fake a back injury and go to a hospital. You will call your grandparents and parents with the same back excuse, hoping they will have Opiate. You will search all night long if you have to, because the Amphetamine comedown hurts that bad. All those embarrassing phone calls in search of Opiate aren't embarrassing at all during this stage, since nothing matters except getting relief from Amphetamine.

Once the Opiate relief comes, then even Opiate isn't enough. You need more of Opiate, so the phone calls continue. When you can't get more of Opiate, you then think about Valium, and how it might even provide more relief, especially when coupled with Opiate.

You don't think you can ever be happy again. The memory causing the happiness flush, coupled with the actual Amphetamine euphoria, took your thinking to unnatural, heightened levels. Therefore, the comedown was a natural disaster.

Nothing has seemed to work! Opiate and Valium did a little, but now your thinking has turned towards regret. Now you want relief from regretful thinking. You reflect on the day's relapse, and now you are embarrassed and ashamed. You think of all the childish manipulation tactics you used and can't help but be ashamed of your actions. You want to turn back to your spiritual ways, but you don't feel worthy to do so. However, you do it anyway, with hopes that the Holy Ghost will come back to you. You pray with all your might for help to come out of this hole you've dug for yourself. You pick up the scriptures and read, hoping to find a powerful concept that will provide you with some safety. You read and pray into the early hours of the morning before you finally feel a hint of light come back into your heart. However, now I'm forcing another memory into your mind, Student: pornography.

Your Fake Friend,

The Devil

MY COLLEAGUE TRANQUILIZER

You need me for stress and sleep.
I will help you to feel tranquil and at peace.

LETTER 19
THE ZAN SLOW DOWN

Dear Student,

I have a friend who can help you with your anxiety and sleep issues. Think about it! You've always liked how Alcohol could lift your spirits and make you more social. But have you ever thought of using Alcohol at night to help you slow down and sleep after being on Amphetamines and Opiates all day? The Amphetamine and Opiate combination offers that speedball effect that won't allow you to sleep.

I see that your relationship with Alcohol has moved forward at a progressive rate; however, his effects seem to be wearing thin. The next day, due to heavy use, has become a bit of a challenge for you. Your head is pounding, and you often feel sick. Your productivity at work and in life has gotten worse, and your overall appearance and well-being are negative.

Student! Why don't you slow down on your Alcohol consumption? I have a better friend for sleep and relaxation, anyway. Her name is Xanax, and she is one of my most beloved and effective friends. Zan is her nickname, and relaxation is her game. She has the ability to slow everything down. She can erase an entire evening. She will take the edge off, making you stress-free . . . at least until she wears off. Your sleep will become better, and in the morning, you won't feel as hungover and sick. You will feel refreshed and ready to take Amphetamine, which will obviously help you climb out of Zan's hole. Keep it all up, Student! You are in a beautiful routine of health.

Your Fake Friend,

The Devil

LETTER 20
FULL OF DREAD

Dear Student,

It's Sunday night, and you seem to be worried about the upcoming workweek. Your heart is beating so fast that it just might burst. Why don't you take something to help slow your mind down? So much is going on in your life, and there is so much that you seem to be dreading.

You are dreading doing paperwork; you are dreading returning phone calls; you are dreading making phone calls; you are dreading replying to emails; you are dreading replying to text messages; you are dreading going to work; you are dreading going to meetings; you are dreading going to the bank; you are dreading paying bills; you are dreading yard work; you are dreading anything and everything that requires you to be responsible. In a sense, you are dreading life. This is comical! How are you going to make it, Student?

You must take something to relieve this stress and anxiety, or you might die. You love what Xanax and Valium are doing for you, but are they doing enough? Student, what about Opiates? Opiates are king, remember? They are more effective in relieving your anxiety anyway. They will allow you to live in the moment and get rid of those suicidal thoughts.

I realize, as of lately, that you've been praying "with all the energy of [your] heart" (Moroni 7:48) to God and Jesus Christ, and they have been whispering in a "still small voice" (1 Nephi 17:45) concerning better ways of dealing with stress. Not sure if you want to go down this road of "[counseling] with the Lord in all thy doings" (Alma 37:37)? This road consists of a long journey full of peaks and valleys. Are you ready for such a hard challenge? My friends and I have been helping you for many years now to deal with stress, and we've been doing a pretty good job for you.

Let's keep this all going, Student! Pleasure is a lot more satisfying than enduring through hardship and pain. Remember, I offer you ways to escape hardship and monotony. Don't be a quitter!

Your Fake Friend,
The Devil

LETTER 21
A NEW HOPE

Dear Student,

Somewhere in the recesses of your mind, God and Jesus Christ—your so-called "Higher Powers"—are saying, "I am the light of the world: he that followeth me shall not walk in darkness, but shall have the light of life" (John 8:12). I know deep down you think this to be true. I can tell that you don't want to take the Opiates, Xanax, and Alcohol. But how are you going to get through this anxiety spell?

There is quite the WAR raging inside your mind. I'm telling you that you can never be free from my grasp or happy without substances. I want you to be "miserable like unto [me]" (2 Nephi 2:27). However, God is encouraging you that "men are, that they might have joy" and that you can experience health, happiness, and euphoric highs without being subject to the whims of me and my team (2 Nephi 2:25).

I realize that, as of lately, you've found hope through scripture study, by "feasting upon the word of Christ" (2 Nephi 31:20). And that the thought of Christ suffering all the pains that you have suffered gives you comfort, knowing that he has "borne [your] griefs, and carried [your] sorrows. . . . And with his stripes [you] are healed" (Isaiah 53:4–5).

Student, do you really believe that you can "humble [yourself] before the Lord, and call on his holy name, and watch and pray continually, that ye may not be tempted above that which ye can bear, and thus be led by the Holy Spirit" (Alma 13:28)? If Christ would never allow you to experience something that you could not handle, why aren't you handling this current moment very well? What's the point in trying to believe this sort of doctrine?

Student! Do you really think that exercise is going to help improve your state of mind? This jogging around the track while giving thanks to God is nonsense. You're working too hard. Even if this does improve your state of mind, there is no way you can stay consistent in such a vigorous effort.

Prayer, coupled with the exercise-induced endorphin lift, helped you climb out of my shadows—for the moment, at least. I can tell you feel more at ease and like your normal self, which I guess is fine for now. I guess you can go back to being the fun-loving dad that you were just yesterday afternoon. I guess you can eat that apple, sit down under a tree, and continue to direct your thoughts toward Christ. Maybe I've been defeated for now! But rest assured, you had better be prepared for my future WAR. I don't like to lose!

Your Fake Friend,
The Devil

SECOND SEMESTER

UNIT 6

POWERLESS

You are powerless.

LETTER 22
YOU ARE POWERLESS

Dear Student,

You can't stop picking up pills from your drug dealer. You can't stop going into the doctor to get more pills. You can't stop spending money. You can't stop lying to your wife. You can't stop dragging your kids around with you to get pills. You can't stop going through people's medicine cabinets. You can't stop smoking Weed and cigarettes. You can't stop taking the pills once you get the pills. You can't stop drinking once you start drinking. You can't stop smoking once you start smoking. You can't stop doing any of my substances once you begin taking them.

Why is this happening, Student? You used to be somewhat moderate. Nowadays, moderation has gone completely out the window.

It seems to me that you have a physical allergy to my substances, which means you are powerless. But are you really powerless, Student? Surely you can do this on your own without the help of a higher power. I know you think you are powerless and that to turn your will and life over to the care of God is the only way for you to gain some power back into your life. But Student, the human mind on its own is a more powerful source.

In the Garden of Eden, God commanded,

Of every tree of the garden thou mayest freely eat,

But of the tree of the knowledge of good and evil, thou shalt not eat of it, nevertheless, thou mayest choose for thyself, for it is given unto thee; but, remember that I forbid it, for in the day thou eatest thereof thou shalt surely die. (Moses 3:16–17)

Therefore, I tempted Adam and Eve, and they "took of the fruit thereof, and did eat" (Genesis 3:6). And after they disobeyed God by eating the fruit, self-will and relapse were introduced into mortality, which meant Adam and Eve were cast out from the presence of the Lord (see D&C 29:40–41). They now had experienced spiritual death and gained the new ability to exercise self-will, which meant they became mortal—subject to physical death—and could, if they so wished, live my lifestyle of pleasure highs that lead to addiction. Or, they could try and "reconcile [themselves] to the will of God, and not to the will of the devil and the flesh," thus turning their will and life back over to the care of God to again return to His presence (2 Nephi 10:24).

There is quite the WAR going on behind the scenes of life, Student. I want you to exercise your self-will, and God wants you to turn your will back over to Him. But remember, God's path means working on your character every day. He wants you to develop the exact character attributes that He has, which is impossible, Student. The high road of God really means "it is better to trust in the Lord than to put confidence in man" (Psalms 118:8). He wants you to learn through the shadows of adversity so that the "inward vessel shall be cleansed first, and then shall the outer vessel be cleansed also" (Alma 60:23). He wants you learning from my substances by quitting my substances in an effort to "clear away the bad according as the good shall grow . . . until the good shall overcome the bad" (Jacob 5:66). He seems to think that if you quit my substances, you will be a great benefit to the world, even an "instrument in the hands of God to bring some soul to repentance" (Alma 29:9). An instrument that He can now use to help others who are struggling.

But Student, isn't God being selfish if that's His plan for you? He's using you just like I'm using you, only He wants you to endure through life's struggle without taking anything. At least through my system of health, I offer immediate relief. His relief only comes after you experience a challenge. It's pleasure or pain, Student. Yours is to choose; after all, "of every tree of the garden thou mayest freely eat" (Genesis 2:16).

Your Fake Friend,

The Devil

LETTER 23
A HIGHER POWER

Dear Student,

That fight with your wife this morning was terrible, yet funny at the same time. The stress from having a nine-month-old baby and a three-year-old daughter, coupled with your substance abuse, has finally hit rock bottom. I'm actually not a fan of rock bottom because that means you just might get motivated enough to climb out. If you are at the bottom, then my preferred next step for you is into the casket. The casket is actually the only rock bottom.

Going down to the temple grounds will do you no good. I know you think that Christ can save you, but he can't. The only hope for you is to continue down my destructive path. These pictures of Christ here at Temple Square mean nothing. I know you feel something, but it's actually nothing. Christ offers hope and stability, right? Wrong!

I think you'll regret trying to get into Christ's way of life. His way of life means pain and endurance. His way of life means learning through adversity. His way of life means boredom and monotony. Student, how are you going to deal with the monotony of life? How will you hang out with your children if you are not high on Opiate? Being a parent is very hard and takes patience. You don't have any patience. How will you go to work and talk to people? Your conversations will be so lame, and your motivation to do anything will be lacking.

There is no way you'll be able to do it. You can try, but you will fail. And then when you fail, people will call you weak. You should be scared of this process because of the chance that you might fail. What will your parents think? What will your wife think? What will your kids think? What will everyone think when you fail? You have always been this cool baseball player, right? You don't want anyone to find out how scared you really are and that you're nothing more than a pathetic drug addict.

Trust me: This is going to be too much work. And embarrassment is sure to happen.

Your Fake Friend,
The Devil

LETTER 24
POWERFUL FOUNDATION

Dear Student,

Since you are headed in this new direction, I feel it necessary to further explain a few things. It is true that, at some point, all of you humans will experience death. Therefore, my competitors—Jesus Christ and His Father, God—enacted the plan of salvation, where Jesus Christ would be born into the flesh to minister among the people and

> go forth, suffering pains and afflictions and temptations of every kind; . . .
>
> And he will take upon him death, that he may loose the bands of death which bind his people; and he will take upon him their infirmities, that his bowels may be filled with mercy, according to the flesh, that he may know according to the flesh how to succor his people according to their infirmities. (Alma 7:11–12).

The claim is that Christ took upon himself the sins of mankind so everyone could enter into the repentance process and be made clean again by being resurrected—spirits reunited with their body—making it so they are now able to return to the presence of God the Father, and His son, Jesus Christ, to live forever (see 1 Corinthians 15:20–22; 2 Nephi 9:6–13).

I tell you this story not to help you, but to warn you. The repentance process is full of high-adventure experiences that require endurance and toughness, because "no unclean thing can inherit the kingdom of heaven" (Alma 11:37). However, challenging life events are sure to happen inside this painful process of repentance; but God has said that "though your sins be as scarlet, they shall be as white as snow; though they be red like crimson, they shall be as wool" (Isaiah 1:18). But Student, keep in mind that this repentance process will provide you with a new knowledge that will lead to great expectations, since knowledge brings a power to which "you may be instructed more perfectly in theory, in principle, in doctrine, [and] in the law of the gospel" (D&C 88:78). And I'm not sure you are prepared to receive this type of knowledge; after you learn it, you'll be held accountable for living it. And living it means "enduring to the end (2 Nephi 31:2), because "God is not mocked: for whatsoever a man soweth, that shall he also reap" (Galatians 6:7). So, Student, the question remains: Are you prepared to compete with me and my team for the remainder of your life?

Again, building your life upon the foundation of Christ brings great expectations. I'm worried that if you choose to do this, your ability to endure through the shadowy mind frame will improve. For so long, I have relied upon my colleagues Depression and Anxiety to help you relapse; but if you have these new coping skills given to you by the Holy Ghost, then I'll have to tempt you from less effective angles, which is bothersome.

The perspective that all adverse events that take place in your life are given to you as learning experiences for your growth towards your Creator; and that "whosoever shall put their trust in God shall be supported in their trials, and their troubles, and their afflictions," seems silly, Student (Alma 36:3). Why would that be the purpose of life? To "[receive] the testimony of Jesus" and be "made perfect through Jesus the mediator of the new covenant, who wrought out this perfect atonement through the shedding of his own blood" so that you could dwell with Him and God in the Kingdom of Heaven for eternity, seems to be a huge thought and expectation, Student (D&C 76:51, 69). Yes, that idea and vast concept seems amazing and in harmony with peaceful, happy feelings, but what if you can't live up to such expectations? After all, "eye hath not seen, nor ear heard, neither have entered into the heart of man, the things which God hath prepared for them that love him" (1 Corinthians 2:9).

Life is unfair! Life is hard! I get the feeling that God just wants you to endure through adversity and not have any fun whatsoever. His leisure would be spent inside the family, seeking after beautiful conversations, and having experiences that are fulfilling and lasting. How much more slow and boring can it all get? There are pills and drinks and sex that can offer so much more of an exciting way of life. You can still be successful and live the "eat, drink, and be merry" lifestyle. There are easier ways around stress.

Student, stay with me!

Your Fake Friend,
The Devil

LETTER 25
ENDURANCE POWER

Dear Student,

Endurance is what makes or breaks you humans. As you search to change your life, there is going to be an endurance period that you will have to go through in order to advance past your old way of life. Student, these challenging life events are going to sting, but I guess if you remain poised and "press forward with a steadfastness in Christ, having a perfect brightness of hope," then you just might make some progress (2 Nephi 31:20). However, the odds are in my favor.

Student, you don't want to deal with life's responsibilities, do you? Things such as paying the bills, fixing your car, or going to work. If you are seriously interested in changing your life, then you are going to have to learn to do things that you don't like to do. My substances have helped you pay the bills, mow the lawn, and run boring errands. Without my substances to help you do these monotonous tasks, what's going to help you? Is God going to help you, Student?

Again, the problem with God is that He encourages learning through failing. He wants you to "bear all these things with patience because the Lord was with thee" and wants you to know "that the Lord did deliver thee" (Alma 38:4). He wants you to lose your temper and then encourages you to fix the character defect that caused you to lose your temper. He wants you to create awareness around how you act, which means He's always going to be asking you to fix your character. And trust me when I tell you this, Student: This will be a life-long process of fixing your character. Until the day you pass from this mortal experience, you will be trying daily to "[put] off the natural man and becometh a saint through the atonement of Christ" (Mosiah 3:19). The natural man inside you is actually my best friend, because the natural man is "easily provoked" and loves pleasure (1 Corinthians 13:5).

How are you to get past the boredom and monotony, Student? Is creativity the answer? Is it to remove boredom from your life by finding that same creative self that used to drive you as a child? These gloomy days that often take over your mind are sad moments, where self-pity becomes your character. To go for a run while listening to inspirational music would portray courage and creativity on some level. I've seen glimpses of this practice from you, Student, and I'm always impressed with your fortitude. Even I, the Devil, can recognize the light that appears inside the shadowy mind. And God has even declared, "if your eye be single to my glory, your whole bodies shall be filled with light, and there shall be no darkness in you" (D&C 88:67).

Student, it's no secret that the mind of the recovering drug addict is going to often be dim, but the secret lies in understanding the big picture of life, which includes God's work of "[succoring] the weak, [lifting] up the hands which hang down, and [strengthening] the feeble knees" (D&C 81:5). I, on the other hand, would have you living your life moment to moment, where you are driven by pleasure. God wants to plant inside you the character that is full of peace, love, and patience. He wants you to capture the type of confidence that will outshine even the darkest of all hours. God wants you to work for Him, Student! He wants you helping others by being a missionary coach in this life and the next. And if you don't "take [His] yoke upon you, and learn of [Him]," then you will not carry the competency to be this missionary coach that He hopes for you to become in this life and the next (Matthew 11:29). But faith is the driving doctrine of God, Student. But because "faith is the substance of things hoped for, the evidence of things not seen," you don't really know for sure if all your hopes and dreams will come true inside God's system of health (Hebrews 11:1). You can hope for a better way of life, but you won't know for sure if it's going to happen. Therefore, you just may "suffer for righteousness' sake" through all of God's learning experiences for no reason at all, other than to experience more pain with little to no reward (1 Peter 3:14).

Unfortunately, inside God's plan of salvation, sadness is what gives you the opportunity to experience happiness because "if there be no righteousness nor happiness there be no punishment nor misery" (2 Nephi 2:13). It is inside the uncomfortable times, Student, that you will come to appreciate the comfortable times, and the long depressing winter is what helps you to appreciate the beauty of the spring and summer. And were it not for the "opposition in all things, . . . righteousness could not be brought to pass, neither wickedness, neither holiness nor misery, neither good nor bad" (2 Nephi 2:11).

If, for example, you are escaping reality frequently through my substances so that you don't have to feel the uncomfortable moments of mortality, then you will never appreciate the comfortable times because you will have been "past feeling [having] given [yourself] over unto lasciviousness, to work all uncleanness with greediness," thus making it impossible for you to appreciate the comfortable times (Ephesians 4:19). And the irony of it all, Student, is that inside the uncomfortable moments of life is where you will learn the most about peace and comfort.

Student, my bet is that you will just keep escaping because, in your mind, the clear life will always be too uncomfortable and stressful. And life will just keep getting more stressful and uncomfortable the longer you go on living in your fake world.

Student, are you ready and willing to "endure to the end" (2 Nephi 31:16)? I don't think you have what it takes to follow "the example of the Son of the Living God" (2 Nephi 31:16).

Your Fake Friend,
The Devil

LETTER 26
RELAPSE POWER

Dear Student,

The thing about "coming unto Christ" is that, by doing so, you take upon yourself His "light which is in all things, which giveth life to all things, which is the law by which all things are governed" (D&C 88:13). Once you capture His light in your heart and soul, you will gain a testimony, which means you will be forever held accountable for having this new knowledge. Then, if you ever choose to turn against what you now know to be true, then you "shall go away into the lake of fire and brimstone, with the devil and his angels" (D&C 76:34–36). I will have you back in my grasp, and it will be even harder to make your way back on top of Christ's foundation. I will, once again, lead you down paths that are more confusing than ever before, and the pleasure and addiction will become far more intense.

If you haven't noticed, I'm talking about relapse, Student—and you will relapse. After a while on this relapse prescription, you will start throwing rocks at Christ and His way of life, which means I'll have you believing that His foundation of health isn't even real or worth it. Pleasure will, once again, take over your life, and it will be far easier to justify your reasoning for returning to live my way of life. Therefore, if this is what's to happen, then why even try, Student?

Is Jesus Christ real? Do you have a loving Heavenly Father? Was there a resurrection? Am I even real, Student? Or is this just all a part of your imagination? "Let no man deceive you by any means: for that day shall not come, except there come a falling away first, and that man of sin be revealed, the son of perdition" (2 Thessalonians 2:3).

I have led many—"a third part of the hosts of heaven" (D&C 29:36)—away from Christ. I even help them forget they ever had a testimony of Jesus Christ. They end up failing to "hearken unto the word of God" and choose to listen to me and my team of spirits instead of Christ and his Holy Spirit (1 Nephi 15:24). They don't have the sure and solid foundation (see Helaman 5:12) to stand on anymore; now, they are trying to build their lives upon my sandy and unstable pleasure foundation. My foundation of health isn't as stable as Christ's, but it's far more fun.

Do you really think that life is a test and proving ground to see if you will keep God's commandments and overcome sin and opposition, Student (see Abraham 3:24–25)? Do you think that those who wander and drift into a life full of sin will "stand before God" to be "judged out of those things which were written in the books, according to their works" (Revelation 20:12)? Will they also be judged "according to the desire of their hearts" (D&C 137:9)? Will the guilt be too much for them to handle?

What about those who, like yourself, are trying to compete in the big show of life by living the commandments of Christ? Will these brave souls have the opportunity to embrace the Savior to go on to "win the prize" (Mosiah 4:27). Or, is it judgmental of you to think like this, Student? Aren't you all supposed to be the same, and no matter how you act in this life, Christ will give out a first-place trophy to all who participated in the game?

But what does it mean to participate in the game, Student? If you think about it, not everyone is "being honest, true, chaste, benevolent, virtuous, and . . . doing good to all men"; not everyone is seeking after "anything virtuous, lovely, or of good report or praiseworthy" (Articles of Faith 1:13). I guess we could safely say that not everyone is playing well in the current game of life. Therefore, why would everyone be given a first-place trophy in the next life? I guess it is obvious that you humans are all involved in some form of a test, which explains light and darkness opposing each other, and "he that keepeth his commandments receiveth truth and light, until he is glorified in truth and knoweth all things" (D&C 93:28).

God even said, "Thou mayest choose for thyself, for it is given unto thee" (Moses 3:17). You can feel me pulling you towards my temptations, but you can also feel God pulling you into the direction of righteous living. If you make the right choices, you increase your ability to make more right choices. If, however, you make the wrong choices, it becomes easier to make more wrong choices. Student, I seek "the misery of all mankind . . . [I] seeketh that all men might be miserable like unto [me] (2 Nephi 2:18, 27). Therefore, there must be "an opposition in all things. If not so, . . . righteousness could not be brought to pass, neither wickedness, neither holiness nor misery, neither good nor bad" (2 Nephi 2:11).

If you think about it, a higher power must've put this system into place so that one day you could be graded on your performance in the great School of Addiction. Those who are righteous get an A in the school and "are received into a state of happiness, which is called paradise, a state of rest, a state of peace, where they shall rest from all their troubles and from all care, and sorrow" (Alma 40:12). Those who are wicked get an F in the school and "have no part nor portion of the Spirit of the Lord; for behold, they chose evil works rather than good; therefore the spirit of the devil [my spirit] did enter into them, and take possession of their house" (Alma 40:13).

Simple enough, right Student? But also confusing enough. Why even bother to try and better yourself? Just stay in hiding behind my substances. Just keep having fun, Student! Everyone is the same, and it doesn't matter how you act in this life. There is no need to work on yourself because salvation was done for you anyway. All you have to do is believe, without trying to change who you are.

Your Fake Friend,
The Devil

LETTER 27
A BOOK OF POWER

Dear Student,

You have found power and truth in a certain book that many will throw stones at. Why believe when many won't? Those "witnesses of the Father and the Son" (2 Nephi 31:18) that come into your heart and mind to reveal "the truth of all things" (Moroni 10:5) when reading such literature are feelings produced by the Holy Ghost. But why listen to a "still small voice" (1 Nephi 17:45) that is lowly and slow to produce results when you could listen to my loud voice of immediate pleasure, thus becoming "past feeling" (1 Nephi 17:45)?

Each day you feast "upon the word of Christ" with hopes of capturing the rewards of peace, ease, and comfort (2 Nephi 31:20). And when I whisper cravings to go and pick up your drug, this book deflects those thoughts and allows you to keep focused on the prize of Christ (see Mosiah 4:27). Apparently, "the fruit of the Spirit is love, joy, peace, longsuffering, gentleness, [and] faith," which for some odd reason seems to now be more valuable rewards to you than any of my pleasures (Galatians 5:22). Student, you used to be so impulsive and impatient, but now you are staying poised and are even showing signs of being fearless. This book seems to be changing you! But the question always remains: Can you keep it all up, Student?

But scripture study can't be the reason for this change taking place in your life. The moving away from my substances and more towards Christ seems to be coming from the reward you are capturing from being involved in righteous living. "For whatsoever ye sow, that shall ye also reap; therefore, if ye sow good ye shall also reap good for your reward" (D&C 6:33). This book floats beautiful concepts into your mind on how to live a better life. These concepts then motivate you to put into action what you have been reading and studying.

I, however, would rather have you

seek not the Lord to establish his righteousness, but [that] every man walketh in his own way, and after the image of his own god, whose image is in the likeness of the world, and whose substance is that of an idol. (D&C 1:16)

The question I have for you, Student, is how a book can have such a unique influence on you, especially when you don't know for a fact that the book is true? What if you are just reading a book that isn't what you think it is? Does it matter to you, Student, that this book might not be true? God even promised,

And when ye shall receive these things, I would exhort you that ye would ask God, the Eternal Father, in the name of Christ, if these things are not true; and if ye shall ask with a sincere heart, with real intent, having faith in Christ, he will manifest the truth of it unto you, by the power of the Holy Ghost. (Moroni 10:4)

I guess this is all a part of God's plan—to allow for you humans to have faith in a process that might not even work. But it does seem to be working in your life, so maybe that does mean it's true, Student. Maybe you've found out the truth—that the only way for you humans to separate from my substances is by using the Atonement of Jesus Christ, "which has been prepared from the foundation of the world, that thereby salvation might come to him that should put his trust in the Lord, and should be diligent in keeping his commandments" (Mosiah 4:6). But again, many find sobriety without God, Student. You could do it on your own will power! You don't need a higher power!

I will never admit that any of this is true, Student. However, most of you humans will not have what it takes to get involved in God's system of healing, because most of you lack the humility. After all, how would one expect to change if they can never admit that they have a problem?

Your Fake Friend,
The Devil

UNIT 7

THE DECISION

You've made the decision.

LETTER 28
GOD'S WILL DECISION

Dear Student,

Most of the world is living my selfish and prideful lifestyle of self-will. You are competitive by nature, but so am I, Student. It was in the premortal council that I competitively said in my heart,

> I will ascend into heaven, I will exalt my throne above the stars of God; I will sit also upon the mount of the congregation, in the sides of the north;
>
> I will ascend above the heights of the clouds; I will be like the Most High.
>
> Yet thou shalt be brought down to hell, to the sides of the pit. (2 Nephi 24:13–15)

This competitiveness that you feel really means pitting yourself against God to "seek [your] own, [and] not the things which are Jesus Christ's" (Philippians 2:21).

God's plan for you humans is to live this higher order of life by providing you with social, security, and sexual instincts. You all want to feel loved and accepted. You all want to be recognized. You all want to think well of yourselves. And you all have plans to gain prestige and acceptance from other humans—all while trying to develop personal relationships by growing your circle of influence to ensure you are secure and safe.

You all want the material wealth and stability that comes from making correct choices. You want to be a leader in many of your social circles, but you also seek to be led and protected by others as well. You humans are an ambitious people, which can lead you to being competitive and hard working. But if that competitive and ambitious spirit becomes the driving force of your life, then your values and goals will slowly shift towards pride. And if you shift into pride, then you will fear social acceptance and will go to great lengths to be noticed. You will then experience contention within your family, will hold grudges against your friends, and won't be able to receive counsel or correction easily. And with all of this comes the want for more material wealth, sex, and substance abuse. Finally, the pressure to keep it all up will be so intense, that fear and insecurity will end up controlling your entire life.

> And they that will harden their hearts, to them is given the lesser portion of the word until they know nothing concerning [God's] mysteries; and then they are taken captive by the devil [me], and led by his will down to destruction. Now this is what is meant by the chains of hell. (Alma 12:11)

Student, think about how many drug addicts my team and I have created simply by using pride and self-will to our advantage. You see, if I can get you to misuse any of these instincts, you end up becoming a victim of my worldly pleasures. Too much money leads to too much pleasure and comfort; too much sex leads to single parenting, abortion, and disease; too much drugs and alcohol leads to ruined families and loss of lives; and too much pride and selfish behavior leads to less charity and more vein desires to "get gain [and] be lifted up one above another" (Helaman 6:17).

All of these basic instincts that God gave you end up causing problems if they are misused, which is why you humans created laws. For some reason, you need accountability partners, or you will turn the world into chaos. The one who drives drunk goes to jail. And the one who hides behind my substances for many years gets left behind in many ways. These are the consequences that I speak of, yet they are small misfortunes compared to the great pleasure escapes my team and I offer. Nothing is more pleasurable than drugs and sex. But there are consequences to having too much sex and drugs. These consequences are worth it because no reward on the planet can match the climax that takes place while using drugs and having sex.

There are only two options that I can see, Student. You either keep trying to exercise my will, which is self-will, or you turn your will over to the care of God and start living His lifestyle by yielding "to the enticings of the Holy Spirit," put off the prideful "natural man," become "a saint through the atonement of Christ the Lord," and become "as a child, submissive, meek, [and] humble" (Mosiah 3:19; see also Alma 13:28).

This means that you must make a decision. But realize that such a decision must be followed up with intense action, which I'm not sure you are ready for. You can make the decision to turn your will over to the care of God—but if you fail to act afterwards, then what's the point? People think things up in their minds every day, Student, but that doesn't mean they act on those thoughts. I don't mind you acting out on the thoughts to use drugs and alcohol, which is, by far, the easier action. After all, my cravings are what drive your habit. But I do mind if you act on the decision to abstain from drugs and alcohol by turning your will over to God, which is the harder action. If you act on the latter decision, then that means you are walking through "the gate, and narrow is the way, which leadeth" to God's path and foundation (Matthew 7:14). That means you are willing to take a hard look at your behaviors and get honest with another person. This means that you are stepping off my unstable, sandy foundation and moving on to a rock-solid foundation of willingness and hope, "whereon if men build they cannot fall" (Helaman 5:12).

Just remember, Student: My way is smooth and full of pleasure. God's way is bumpy and full of pain. If you do choose to act on this decision, you should know that your future days will be full of blood, sweat, and tears.

Your Fake Friend,
The Devil

LETTER 29
OPIATE OR GOD DECISION

Dear Student,

Nothing can make you feel as warm and safe as my friend and colleague Opiate does. You remember how proactive he makes you feel, right? Lately, you have been trying to replace the Opiate warmth with the gospel of Jesus Christ, to be "clasped in the arms of Jesus," with hopes of feeling safe and warm again (Mormon 5:11). I know you are trying to develop faith in the Atonement of Christ, even "[hoping] for things which are not seen, which are true" (Alma 32:21).

My competitor is promoting that you become a "new creature" by putting off my lifestyle and taking on His instead (2 Corinthians 5:17). Is Christ's lifestyle really that much more beautiful than mine? His way is slow to develop and takes work; mine is immediate gratification and takes no work. His is linked to meekness and lasting happiness; mine is linked to loud laughter and pleasure. His fun is linked to challenge. My fun is linked to a roller coaster ride where I'll take you up fast, but down even faster.

Now, after all that comparing, can you honestly tell me that His way of life seems more fun than mine?

What is to become of your children? Don't think I don't hear you trying to teach them how to live the lifestyle of Christ, even taking them to church with you. My hope is to get your family away from the gospel of Jesus Christ, but I can see now that I must take a different approach in order to make this happen. Don't get it twisted: Your kids will remember your drug-addicted ways. They remember you nodding out on the couch. They remember your irritability towards them and their mother. They remember your up-and-down mood. They remember driving around with you from ATM to ATM to get cash to fund more pills. They remember the fights with their mother. They remember the financial insecurity. They remember all of it and more. This is how the disease gets spread inside the family: It's the trauma of them seeing all of the aforementioned. Therefore, a good chance still exists for them to end up on my team instead of Christ's.

My goal is to entrap your children in the snares of the world. I want them looking at pornography and involved in "fleshly lusts, which war against the soul" (1 Peter 2:11). I want them participating in immoral behavior. I want them wrapped up in drugs and alcohol addiction. I want them off of Christ's straight and narrow path and into my pit, where only misery and sadness can be found.

I don't at all promise the peaks or abundant life like my competitor, Jesus Christ, does. He keeps on pushing the same consistent and boring theme: that of a life filled with abundance and high-adventure experiences where no fear, harms, or resentments exist. How can this be true? Are you really going to believe that you can actually participate in a life that is free from contention, worry, anxiety, and stress? Life is full of this sort of material, and the only way to escape it is through my substances. He is asking way too much work of you. How free do you want to be? Well, not free enough if you are lazy and lack diligence, which I will do everything in my power to promote. After all, "the soul of the sluggard desireth, and hath nothing: but the soul of the diligent shall be made fat" (Proverbs 13:4).

Your Fake Friend,
The Devil

LETTER 30
DECISION TO PRAY

Dear Student,

If you haven't realized it by now, I am that great and terrible spirit of opposition and contention. My ways are subtle, but you can still identify them:

> But whatsoever thing persuadeth men to do evil, and believe not in Christ, and deny him, and serve not God, then ye may know with a perfect knowledge it is of the devil; for after this manner doth the devil work, for he persuadeth no man to do good, no, not one; neither do his angels; neither do they who subject themselves unto him. (Moroni 7:17)

My plan is to interrupt those promptings that come from the Holy Ghost. The "still small voice" is easy for me to talk over, so go ahead and try to "hearken unto the Spirit which teacheth a man to pray" (2 Nephi 32:8). Prayer is oftentimes a repetitive practice that usually means nothing. People all over the planet have tried to get into prayer in the same way you are, yet they end up failing miserably. These pathetic humans often start out strong, with a great desire to live the lifestyle of Christ, but end up lacking the diligence to keep it all up. I'm sure you will be the same, Student.

They talk of diligence as being this zealous and consistent effort that will lead one to find the lifestyle of Christ. Diligence is the mother of good luck, right? It takes diligence to "believe in Christ and deny him not" (2 Nephi 25:28). It takes diligence to trust in Christ and not in the arm of the flesh (see 2 Nephi 4:34). But Student, are you diligent enough to "come unto Christ, and be perfected in him" (Moroni 10:32)? Are you humble enough to come "with a broken heart and a contrite spirit," even hungering and thirsting after righteousness (3 Nephi 12:6, 19)? Are you willing to "[feast] upon the word of Christ" by reading the scriptures daily (2 Nephi 31:20)?

But Student, you have been diligent to my lifestyle for a great number of years now; and you do have an all-or-nothing personality, which isn't a bad thing. In baseball, it led you far, but when I introduced you to my friends of substance, you went all in with them as well. Student! You've been blessed with great diligence anyway, so why bother to capture more of it?

This nighttime "[praying] unto the Father" in the name of Jesus Christ to help you keep it all up is dangerous (3 Nephi 18:19). You seem to be actually talking and pleading with God instead of saying some repetitive prayer with no "real intent of heart . . . [that] profiteth [you] nothing, for God receiveth none such" (Moroni 7:9). I'll have to admit that the seriousness of your praying, "with all the energy of heart," is a great concern for me and my team (Moroni 7:48). Again, Student, I would rather have you use "vain repetitions" when you pray (see Matthew 6:7).

No more jogging and praying. No more walking and praying. No more nighttime prayers in the stairwell. No more praying while staring at the stars. No more praying with your wife and kids. If you are going to pray, then do so in a hurried way and don't pretend to "live in thanksgiving daily, for the many mercies and blessings which he doth bestow upon [you]" (Alma 34:38).

After all, how do you know that God is even there? Well, I guess, if I am here, then God would have to be real as well. Do I even exist, Student? Or is this all just your imagination? Maybe there is no such thing as a higher and lower power. Maybe you humans are all here by mistake. If that's the case, then you should live life to the fullest amount of pleasure because this is all you got. The casket is next. And after the casket, nothing but blackness.

But go ahead and keep "[crying] unto God for all thy support." Go ahead and keep "[counseling] with the Lord in all thy doings" with a hope that "he will direct thee for good." Go ahead and pray "unto the Lord, that he may watch over you in your sleep; and when thou risest in the morning let thy heart be full of thanks unto God" (Alma 37:36–37).

But again, is God really listening?

Your Fake Friend,

The Devil

LETTER 31
DECISION TO SEE

Dear Student,

Maybe it is true that the mortal experience truly is full of high-adventure experiences, where there is "opposition in all things. If not so, . . . righteousness could not be brought to pass, neither wickedness, neither holiness nor misery, neither good nor bad" (2 Nephi 2:11). I find it interesting how God asks you to endure through the rugged terrain of life while at the same time appreciating the beauty inside the struggle. He even said, "my people must be tried in all things, that they may be prepared to receive the glory that I have for them" (D&C 136:31).

The monotonous life experience is actually beautiful when one contemplates the miracle of forgiveness and how God's "arm of mercy is extended towards you, and whosoever will come, him will [God] receive; and blessed are those who come unto [him]" (3 Nephi 9:14). Basically, you humans have it so good, and you don't even realize it. A beautiful plan of happiness and forgiveness has been put in place for "all ye that labour and are heavy laden, and [God] will give you rest" (Matthew 11:28). And all I keep hearing from you humans is how boring and monotonous life is. If I would've gotten my way, no free agency would have been experienced, which means you would be boring robots instead of those who can create art. Student, how boring can life really be if you have the ability to "act for yourselves—to choose the way of everlasting death or the way of eternal life" (2 Nephi 10:23)? But let's be honest: God's ways are boring compared to my fast pleasures.

God wants you looking at scenery and appreciating the sunsets even if the adversity in your life seems unbearable. These roadblocks that often form in your mind are what blind you from being grateful for the simple things in life. God promised, "he who receiveth all things with thankfulness shall be made glorious" (D&C 78:19). I, on the other hand, would have you building up resentful scenarios in your mind about colleagues who have appeared to threaten you. This mean dialogue leads you to selfish and resentful thoughts that make it nearly impossible for you to feel grateful and charitable. Until you stop competing with other people's pride—regardless of how nice you appear to others on the outside—you will remain in a constant state of negative chaos inside your mind. Everyone sees you as being a great man, Student, but what they don't see is who you are on the inside. You have a lot of work to do, which is why I'm not threatened by giving you these answers.

Your Fake Friend,

The Devil

UNIT 8

BLOCKED FROM GOD

Why can't you feel the spirit?

LETTER 32
BLOCKED FROM FAITH

Dear Student,

I fear that your current mental state is a challenging one. I doubt that your thinking will ever go back to a happy frame of mind. My substances do have that effect on people. The years of Amphetamine and Opiate abuse have depleted your dopamine, and now you can't feel any joy whatsoever. There is no fix for this, Student. This is a permanent mindset that you cannot escape.

Skiing is so boring; fishing is so boring; hanging out at home is so boring. Doing any of your past hobbies just isn't the same, is it? You used to be able to have fun before the substance abuse; but now, no such feelings exist. Life is just so mundane and flat, which is why it would just be better for you to remain in a relationship with my substances.

I know that God is promising you "a firm hope that ye shall one day rest from all your afflictions" (Alma 34:41). He claims that the repentance process can heal your mind by giving you the Holy Ghost as a "Comforter" (John 14:26) who will inevitably fill you "with hope and perfect love" (Moroni 8:26) and "teach you the peaceable things of the kingdom" (D&C 36:2). But Student, in order to receive the Holy Ghost into your system, you will first have to get rid of those practices that block you from God, for "no unclean thing can dwell with God" (1 Nephi 10:21). How do you expect to get rid of your resentments and fears? And what about all the harm you have done to others? Currently, your mind is full of resentments, anger towards others, comparisons, jealousies, and insecurities, not to mention obsessive worry about how you've harmed others. Your mind is a mess, and I don't see you having the ability, nor the fortitude, to grow past this mindset. In order to get rid of this brain storm, you would have to work on changing how you think. When resentful, jealous, and fearful thoughts arise, you would have to ask God to remove them, and to "create in [you] a clean heart

. . . and renew a right spirit within [you]" (Psalm 51:10). But do you really believe that He is just going to remove them without you trying to remove them first? That is what I can't understand about God and His doctrine: He asks you to pray to him, but He also asks you to be "doers of the word, and not hearers only," which means you must work on changing your thoughts and behavior, while God slowly helps you make progress out of my shadows (James 1:22). Again, He wants you to gain a learning experience while you struggle and fumble around in the dark. Learning takes place inside adversity, right?

When you are fearful, God says that "if ye will have faith in me ye shall have power to do whatsoever thing is expedient in me" (Moroni 7:33). Fear and faith, as I understand it, Student, cannot exist in the same room, so either faith must be driving your behavior, or fear will step in and do it for you. I am one to promote fear, because fear is a true principle that protects people. Who is to say having faith in a higher power will help you "withstand every temptation of the devil, with their faith on the Lord Jesus Christ" (Alma 37:33)? Also, Student, keep in mind that faith is linked to works. So, if you have faith, you must be working on aligning your way of life with Jesus Christ's. You must have a great "desire to believe," which will "give place" for the word to be "planted in your heart"; and then "ye shall reap the rewards of your faith, and your diligence, and patience, and long-suffering" (Alma 32:26–43). And now, you believe that you "can do all things through Christ which strengtheneth [you]" (Philippians 4:13).

This all seems so silly to me, Student. Why would God ask you to work out your own salvation when it is "by grace are ye saved through faith" (Ephesians 2:8)? Wasn't salvation that gift He gave to you freely? Therefore, can't you just sit around and wait for God to change you? Or do you really believe that it takes personal effort and "that [you] are saved, after all [you] can do" (2 Nephi 25:23)?

Your Fake Friend,

The Devil

LETTER 33
BLOCKED FROM PEACE

Dear Student,

Fear and resentment are part of life. Why do you think you've made so much progress in competitive sports throughout your life? It was your resentments and fears that caused you to work harder than most. You just hated the thought of someone out-working or being better than you, which led you to accomplish much throughout your sports career.

You've always wanted to stand out amongst your peers and colleagues. And now I see you trying to get rid of your resentful, fearful, and competitive mind frame. Why, Student? This is who you are. This is the special part of self that God gave you: the great talent that not everyone has. This competitive character is what has been driving your success all along, and now you are trying to remove it. This makes no sense, Student.

I fear that this new discovery about yourself will lead you to the realization that you aren't as special as you've always thought. This could be a heartbreaking discovery for you, Student. You may discover that it was your ego and selfishness that have been driving your behavior all along. You've always been able to get what you want, right? Throughout your entire life, you have manipulated situations so that everything works in your favor. This selfishness and ego lead you to massive resentments that dominate your mind to the point of not being able to turn your will and life over to the care of God because you have instead turned your will and life over to the people you are resenting.

If we are getting honest, Student—and we are—fear has also played a similar role in your life. It's almost pathetic how much you have feared failure. Isn't fear the reason you've worked so hard? Your fear of failure has dominated your mind for most of your life. You felt stupid when you were a kid because you weren't good at school, which is why you went on to obtain a master's degree in business. You wanted to show everyone that you weren't stupid, right? It's the "I told you so" mentality. "I have a master's degree and you don't!" "I played college and professional baseball and you didn't!" "I'm special and different!" These are the thoughts that have driven your success, Student.

It was the same in sports, right? Student, if I was observing correctly, and I believe I was, you didn't even really like sports. Weren't you just afraid to let everyone down by telling them that you didn't like competing in sports? Your dad was good at sports, so you had to be good at sports, right? The common theme for your life has been a fear of failure. How pathetic, Student!

The game you are about to enter is, by far, the most competitive game you have ever played in. What I see you trying to do is starting a competition with yourself. For so long, you have been hiding behind my substances, which has made it easy for you to escape any type of competition with yourself. You haven't needed to abstain from drugs, alcohol, smoking, or even food. It's just easier to stay on my side. I don't want you being competitive with yourself, but I do want you competing with other people's pride. Aren't you jealous of what everyone else has? But on the other hand, don't try to improve yourself. Just sit inside your resentments and mope around feeling sorry for yourself.

Your Fake Friend,
The Devil

LETTER 34
BLOCKED FROM HAPPINESS

Dear Student,

Taking the time to write down all of your fears, harms, and resentments is a waste of time. In fact, you should fear this process because of all the hard feelings that will arise within you as you put it all down on paper. Why would you want to revisit all of your harms and admit to all of your fears?

You are a competitive person, Student. You have always been competitive, which is why you've always excelled in sports. The mentality of hoping for other people's failures so you can appear better than them serves you, right? You want to be the best, you are special, and you are far different than everybody else.

Your greatest fear seems to be of being ordinary. You will never have to worry about being ordinary because you are better than everyone else. Your peers and past friends do nothing but judge you. They see how you've been in a relationship with my substances, and they speak ill of you behind your back. It's tough not to resent how much of the material world they have obtained. They have the boats, they have the house, they have the cars, and they have the perfect family on social media. You, on the other hand, lost your house, have bad credit, and your posts on social media regarding your perfect family are fake. Let's be honest: You and your wife's relationship is more cold than hot. I mean, how could it be otherwise? You have been selfish, Student!

So, now you want to write all of these fears, harms, and resentments down on paper and then review them with another person. You have some deep-rooted trauma that happened to you as a child that I'm not sure you should share with another person. You have some harms that you have committed towards others that shouldn't ever be mentioned.

Arc you really wanting to "let your sins trouble you . . . which shall bring you down unto repentance" (Alma 42:29–30)?

This will be a long process because you fear everything, Student. You fear failure. You fear success. You fear relapse. You fear monotony and boredom. You fear speaking in front of people. You fear the banks and creditors. You fear not being a good dad and husband. You fear just about everything. There seems to be no way out of these fears—unless, of course, you allow God to replace your fears with His faith so that you can "run with patience the race that is set before [you]" (Hebrews 12:1). But even then, Student, there is no guarantee that these fears will be removed, because faith means believing something good will develop so long as you turn your will and life over to the care of God and realize that only "after much tribulation come the blessings" (D&C 58:4). It's believing something beautiful will happen in your life as long as you put pressure towards God's way of life and are not "idle; for he that is idle shall not eat the bread nor wear the garments of the laborer" (D&C 42:42). That means having faith in God, Student. That means trying to believe in a power greater than yourself; a power that you will never be able to prove tangibly. You will have to have faith, and then "put [your] trust in God," and you will be "supported in [your] trials, and [your] tribulations, and [your] afflictions" (Alma 36:6).

But what is God's lifestyle? Let's first talk about everything that His lifestyle isn't. His lifestyle isn't the immediate pleasures that come from pills, smokes, and drinks. His lifestyle isn't fast, loud, and full of laughs. His lifestyle isn't full of dishonesty, manipulations, and deceit. His lifestyle isn't full of fear and resentment. His lifestyle isn't being mad and holding grudges toward others. His lifestyle isn't being impatient and prideful. The lifestyle of Christ is in the opposite direction of all these things, which is a daunting agenda, to say the least.

Turning your will over to Christ means doing the opposite of all of that and more. He wants less pleasure and more endurance. He wants you to slow down and stay present. He wants you to be honest and persuasive. He wants you to forgive yourself and others. He wants you to be full of patience and humility. And he wants you to "take [his] yoke upon you, and learn of [him]; for [he] [is] meek and lowly in heart: and ye shall find rest unto your souls" (Matthew 11:29).

Wouldn't it be easier to just stay on the world's side? Sounds like turning your will over to God means gambling on a way of life that might not even be real. You know my way of life is real because you have lived it. Faith might not even be real, Student.

But go ahead and create your list and go be honest about your past way of life to another person. This may or may not lead you to being free from those thoughts and harms that have been blocking you from the "Sunlight of the Spirit" all along. What do you really have to lose by trying? Even if you do capture a spiritual awakening, I still have other plans for you. And anyway, remaining spiritually fit takes diligence and work, and I don't think you have what it takes to keep it all up.

Your Fake Friend,
The Devil

LETTER 35
BLOCKED FROM THE TRUTH

Dear Student,

I see that you are on the verge of finding the truth out about yourself. You first found out that the true problem behind your so-called addictions was related to your powerlessness over me and my team of substances. I actually like the idea of me having so much power over you—so much power that you were forced to search for the truth about God. I know you think He is the truth behind all things, but Student, we have talked about this type of faith before!

If you are powerless over me, then God must be that higher power that can restore you to sanity:

> He created all things, both in heaven and in earth; …he has all wisdom, and all power, both in heaven and in earth; …[and] man doth not comprehend all the things which the Lord can comprehend. (Mosiah 4:9)

Is that the truth or not, Student? How do you know that "if thou believest in the redemption of Christ thou canst be healed" (Alma 15:6)? How do you know that God is the truth if you don't even know that He exists? Student! Again, the question remains: Do I even exist?

This decision you've made to turn your life over to the care of God could be foolish and far from the truth. If you act on this decision, how does this prove the truth about God? Yes, you could say that "all things denote there is a God; yea, even the earth, and all things that are upon the face of it, yea, and its motion, yea, and also all the planets which move in their regular form do witness that there is a supreme Creator" (Alma 30:44). It could even be said that there is a unique spirit that's been inside the human race since the beginning of time that often whispers insight concerning the great plan of a Creator. Many have called this spirit the light of Christ, which "proceedeth forth from the presence of God to fill the immensity of space." It is "the light which is in all things, which giveth life to all things, which is the law by which all things are governed" (D&C 88:12–14; see also verses 6–11). This light has the capability to radiate from the soul of every human born onto this planet. But why so much violence and sad situations if there is a Creator who has a plan for His children? Why is it when you humans exercise self-will with reckless abandon that this light of Christ gets blocked out? Is it because "the Spirit of Christ is given to every man, that he may know good from evil" and "every thing which inviteth to do good, and to persuade to believe in Christ, is sent forth by the power and gift of Christ" (Moroni 7:16)?

Think about it! No matter how much self-will you exercise, I'm the one who sticks with you. To say my pleasure way of life blocks you from the light of Christ is nonsense. These resentments and fears that you carry are a part of the human plight. Just like I've mentioned before, these resentments are why you've made so much progress in your life. Resentments are another way of staying competitive, Student. You are competitive, and there is nothing wrong with that.

But to write down all of these fears, resentments, and harms in an effort to find out the truth about yourself is quite interesting. So now I ask you this: What type of behavior and thoughts have been blocking you from accessing the light of Christ? I find it odd that you must be living the lifestyle of Christ or He won't afford you the opportunity to capture a spiritual experience. Isn't that selfish on His part? Basically, in order to capture the "Sunlight of [his] Spirit," you must remove those fears, resentments, and harms so you can become free from the "bondage of self." In doing so, you are now capable of experiencing God's will working in your life instead of being driven by self-will. Are you serious about going after these types of truths, Student?

And what about this idea of sharing your list of resentments, harms, and fears with another person? Don't you have enough of the truth? How much more pain do you have to cause yourself? To say that you need an outsider to help you see the real truth about your behavior is absurd. Your prayers to God about your list were one thing, but to involve another person would really be selfish on your end. If you are truthful in that confession, then what is to come of your shame and guilt? I mean, how does confessing your sins help you make positive changes in your life? God even says, "I, the Lord, forgive sins unto those who confess their sins before me and ask forgiveness" (D&C 64:7).

For all these years, Student, you have been blaming other people yet failing to look at the part you may have played. You did this as a way to protect yourself against getting hurt, which makes perfect sense. Your addiction is the doctors' fault because they told you how to take the pills but failed to tell you how to stop taking them. They over-prescribed you, right? Also, you are a different thinker than everyone else; therefore, you are justified in carrying around self-pity. No one understands what you have been going through, right? Your family and friends just don't get you. You are different than them, so it's okay that you're always thinking about yourself. Your good friends of the past just can't understand why you isolate and act as if they don't matter anymore. But the reason you struggle with addiction is because they enabled you to keep partying, drinking, smoking, and taking pills. Student, can you blame them? Nobody really likes being around the sober you. It was their fault, and you have every reason in the world to be resentful towards them.

Your Fake Friend,

The Devil

THE GAME
OF LIFE

The competition is against one's self.

LETTER 36
COMPETE AGAINST YOURSELF

Dear Student,

Are you willing to compete with yourself from here on out? You first started competing with yourself when you saw the problem, realized the solution, and then made the all-important decision to turn your life over to the care of God. But what was most impressive was when you wrote down those behaviors and thoughts that were blocking you from the Holy Spirit. Then you had the courage to share all those harms, fears, and resentments with another person. I'm truly impressed, Student.

But Student, these character defects of which you are trying to get rid have been developed through practice. You have been diligent, Student!

But are you now willing enough to let go of all these character defects and be "diligent in keeping the commandments of God" (Alma 7:23)? These are trained thoughts and behaviors that aren't going to be easy to get rid of. The up-and-down mood, the control, the fears, and the resentments are just a few of the many defects that have become a part of you. You have become the impatient man who is full of negative energy and resentful thoughts towards others. Now you're asking God to remove these character defects. Do you think it's just going to happen when you ask in prayer? If you do, then you aren't as smart as I thought you were, Student, because "faith without works is dead" (James 2:20).

It all goes back to God wanting you to let go of your old self by working hard to become a "new creature" in Christ, which means now throughout your days, you'll have to challenge your thoughts (2 Corinthians 5:17). When fear crops up, you'll have to ask God to remove fear and replace it with faith, since fear and faith cannot work together. When resentment and scenarios start to take up space in your brain, you will have to compete against those thoughts by asking God to help you rcmove them and instead "let virtue garnish thy thoughts unceasingly" (D&C 121:45).

This idea that of regularly thinking, acting, and reacting differently to daily life adversity seems silly. Practice makes perfect, right? God has put in front of you the unrealistic expectation that you should try to be perfect, "even as your father which is in heaven is perfect" (Matthew 5:48). But we all know that you can't be perfect; in order for you to change in such a dramatic way, some type of spiritual overhaul must take place in your heart and mind. What's the plan then, Student?

Is your plan to practice thinking better? In baseball, you practiced, which led you to become a good baseball player. You weren't a perfect baseball player, but you were good. When you failed and had bad games, you made adjustments and moved on. Is this your strategy to change your thinking as well?

The problem I see with your thinking is that it has molded your personality. You've been thinking and acting this way for so long that I wonder if it's possible to change. When an irrational and negative thought comes into your mind, how are you going to change it? I guess you now have a new awareness around your thoughts and actions from when you wrote them down and examined them with another person. You seem to have somewhat of an idea concerning the thoughts you need to compete with in order to keep your spiritual condition high. I guess you're on the right track, Student. But I'm always going to question if you have what it takes to change your thinking. This means every hour of every day, you are going to have to practice thinking differently by nourishing the word "by your faith with great diligence, and with patience" (Alma 32:41–43). When someone cuts you off in traffic, then you must wave and "[work] patience" (James 1:3–4). When someone speaks ill of you, you must be forgiving "even as God for Christ's sake hath forgiven you" (Ephesians 4:32). When you feel like being in a hurry and ornery, you will have to slow down to be patient and "kind, . . . tenderhearted, forgiving one another" (Ephesians 4:32). When a friend or colleague snubs you, you will have to let go of your pride and "humble [yourself] as [a] little child" (Matthew 18:4). And when resentment and fear raise their ugly heads, you'll have to carry more love and faith than ever before, "thus [being] led by the Holy Spirit, becoming humble, meek, submissive, patient, full of love and all long-suffering" (Alma 13: 28–29).

These are tall orders, Student. I guess it makes sense that, if you want to change your thoughts, then you have to try and change your thoughts. This new thinking that you are trying to capture really means a higher order of thinking that's linked to "the pure love of Christ" (Moroni 7:47). To change your thinking means changing your habitual thinking. For some reason, you have found comfort in trying to control and manipulate everything, which is why you fear and resent everyone and everything. In a sense, you crave control, which is why you have gotten in the habit of thinking this way. In order to change your thinking, you'll have to crave a new mindset, since craving drives habit. You'll have to "feast upon the words of Christ; for behold, the words of Christ will tell you all things what ye should do" (2 Nephi 32:3).

But Student, how are you going to crave a new mindset if you don't have any rewards to seek after? Are the rewards of Christ enticing enough to satisfy your cravings? Your thinking has been dark and well-rehearsed for years. You seek new rewards, but what's the plan for capturing these new rewards that lead to this higher order of thinking?

Your Fake Friend,

The Devil

LETTER 37
COMPETE AGAINST CRAVINGS

Dear Student,

My team and I almost caused you to relapse yesterday. Things have been going great with you and your wife, and if you would've relapsed, dishonesty and trust issues would've come back into the picture.

You see, Student, the reward for Opiate will always be there in your mind regardless of how long you go without him. The sense of ease and comfort that he provides is far more powerful than any type of reward that God can provide.

Yesterday, however, you surprised me. Usually, when the craving for Opiate burrows deep down in your mind, the reward becomes too heavy to handle. Then the habit loop starts all over when you relapse. The pattern, in the past, has been for you to lay around and watch Netflix, even feeling sorry for yourself with hopes that the craving will go away, but it never does. You always end up at the doctor's office to capture your Opiate reward.

But not yesterday. Yesterday, you decided to go for a scenic trail run instead. And while you were jogging, I heard you praying to God the entire time so that you could not "be tempted by the devil, [to] be led away captive" (3 Nephi 18:15). You had inspirational music playing, and you saw some scenery that caused you to deeply "ponder the path of life" (Proverbs 5:6). As you turned the intensity up for lap three, "the peace of God [began to] rule in your heart," while tears of thankfulness streamed down your face for family, friends, and even God (Colossians 3:15). As you paced back and forth while cooling down, you captured the reward you were looking for, which was a brighter reward than the Opiate reward. The craving for Opiate was gone, and the new reward inside your soul was charity and feelings of accomplishment from having the "pure love of Christ" running through your system (Moroni 7:47). The Holy Spirit pushed me and my team out of your mind and heart and provided you with a sense of peace and comfort, to which the "remission of sins bringeth meekness, and lowliness of heart; and because of meekness and lowliness of heart cometh the visitation of the Holy Ghost" (Moroni 8:26).

I'll have to admit, this is impressive work, Student. I did not think you had it in you to create a spiritual experience in the way that you did. The endorphin lift from the exercise, coupled with the music and scenic views, created the perfect platform for you to communicate with God. He was able to climb inside your heart and help you capture the reward of peace and security. Once again, He always asks you to work for His rewards—but it worked. I guess it does work if you are willing to put in the effort.

Anyway, this is just a small setback for me and my team because chances are you won't be diligent enough to keep this all up.

Your Fake Friend,
The Devil

LETTER 38

COMPETE AGAINST POOR MINDSET

Dear Student,

I see what you're are trying to do, but I still don't understand how you are going to replace your current selfish, resentful, and fearful mindset with a better one. The rewards that my substances have offered you these past years are deeply ingrained within your mind. They've even helped create your current character—or character defects, I should say.

Student, how familiar are you with how you currently think and act? There is comfort inside this routine you've been holding down for all these years, and to try and change it means discomfort. I've rarely seen anyone change how they think, but I guess you can keep trying to kill off your old ideas and replace them with new ones. It was once said, "Therefore if any man be in Christ, he is a new creature: old things are passed away; behold, all things are become new" (2 Corinthians 5:17).

How do people really change their behavior, Student? There seem to be so many reservations in the human mind that it becomes nearly impossible. The ones who have changed worked tirelessly on repairing their character defects. If you think about it, Student, the human character starts off innocent and perfect as children do, but as people grow into adults, the world and its shiny objects create holes in their characters. That is what has happened to you, Student. I guess if you want to change bad enough, then you'll have to gain the courage to give up on your current character and begin the journey of creating a new one.

As of lately, I've seen ideas float into your mind about orchestrating stress in a way that would force you to get uncomfortable. This new mindset that you are chasing after will only work if you are accepting of new ideas. God says that "if men come unto [him, He] will show unto them their weakness" and that he gives men weakness "that they may be humble" (Ether 12:27). So, when resentment creeps in, Student, you'll have to push such thoughts out and replace them with thoughts of forgiveness and love, because to "love is of God" (1 John 4:7). You may have to call someone and have them help you sort through your resentments and fears, which is outside of your comfort zone anyway. I love how you are so twisted up all of the time inside your mind. You're always wondering if people like you and if your best is ever good enough. This always leads you to feeling fearful.

Student, do you really think it's possible to change these thoughts that have been on repeat for ten-plus years now? No way, Student! Yes, you can force them out and practice your positive affirmations. You can start giving everyone the benefit of the doubt by trying to see them in a positive light instead of a negative one. You can try and stop being so competitive and resentful against others who have achieved more than you and start being happy for them instead. You can even stop trying to control all situations and let your God handle them. But again, such discomfort is not for the faint of heart. The only people who end up surviving on this repentance journey are those who can get comfortable sitting in the shadows by "[enduring] to the end, [and] following the example of the Son of the living God," while at the same time "[pressing] forward with a steadfastness in Christ, having a perfect brightness of hope, and a love of God and of all men" (2 Nephi 31:16, 20).

Each day, you will have to practice thinking and acting this way, Student. You will have to be "watching and praying continually, that [you] might be delivered from [me], and from death, and from destruction" (Alma 15:17). You will have to be listening to audiobooks and "[feasting] on the words of Christ; for behold, the words of Christ will tell you all things what ye should do" (2 Nephi 32:3). You will have to be going to meetings often, "both to pray and to hear the word of the Lord" (4 Nephi 1:12). You will have to be calling upon trusted people for advice, and also "[counseling] with the Lord in all thy doings" in order for this new way of thinking to come forth (Alma 37:37).

Again, need I remind you that my reward system far outshines God's reward system? My habits are easy to capture because they are immediate. God's habits are hard to capture because they are linked to work and take time to develop. You won't see God's rewards because they are subtle. You will see my rewards immediately because I will take you up immediately. And Student, don't worry about when I drop you into "that lake of fire and brimstone, whose flames are unquenchable" (Jacob 6:10). Trust me when I tell you that God won't be there either.

I know you think that if you involve yourself in hard things by taking Christ's "yoke upon you" (Matthew 11:29), you will capture the rewards of confidence, self-esteem, and "peace, where [you] shall rest from all [your] troubles and from all care, and sorrow" (Alma 40:12). You will feel accomplished, right? You just may create new thought patterns that lead to new cravings. Most people think that you can only crave my substances. But if you involve yourself in this God-conscious mindset, then you will end up craving His way of life. Then, new habits are sure to form. Remember, cravings drive habit, Student! If you find out that God's rewards are far more lasting and peaceful than my rewards, then a new way of life for you is sure to come forth. Of that, I have no doubt.

But I'm not worried at all, Student. If you quit one habit, I'll have another one for you to quit soon after. Remember, this is a life of trying and quitting. Do quitters really prosper? Or are they just quitters? Don't be a quitter, Student. Keep playing my game.

Your Fake Friend,
The Devil

LETTER 39
COMPETE FOR LOVE

Dear Student,

Let's make a comparison, shall we? If you let go of fear, courage is sure to follow. And if you cut all ties with resentful thinking, love and tolerance will take its place. I guess God has put into place for you humans a pattern for living, and if you live in such a way, then peace and happiness will come into your life.

On my end, however, resentments are what make you competitive. They make you who you are, Student. We've already discussed this at length, but as I see you competing with and challenging your resentful thinking, I feel it is necessary to try and guide you back to being competitive. Yes, it is quite right that love, tolerance, patience, courage, humility, and wisdom are all principles of truth that no one could argue about not being beneficial to the human personality. But, if you capture this new type of character, you are sure to be taken advantage of, Student.

God wants you to have love for one another. His second great commandment is to "love thy neighbour as thyself" (Matthew 22:39). But His first great commandment is to "love the Lord thy God with all thy heart, and with all thy soul, and with all thy mind" (Matthew 22:37). I wonder if you can truly love your neighbor without loving God first? He claims that having the "pure love of Christ" running through your system means peace and happiness "and whoso is found possessed of it at the last day, it shall be well with him" (Moroni 7:47). But I would argue that peace and happiness are a byproduct of protecting yourself against people, places, and things. If you stop worrying about those things that are out of your control, then what remains of your reality, Student? I guess you would now make an entrance into the present moment, but what good would that do you? Student, I don't think you would know how to handle the present moment, to "meditate upon these things; [and] give thyself wholly to them" (1 Timothy 4:15). It just may scare you to find out how simple life really is and how easy it is to love yourself and other people.

Let's start with the love you have for yourself, Student. Do you even like who you are? And if not, how would you expect to love anyone else? Your own self-hatred is a reflection of selfishness. Can't you see that your own selfishness is the reason why you hate yourself? All these years, you have been looking inward at your own special self without realizing that those around you have problems as well. I'm sorry to tell you that you aren't the only one who has had problems, Student. Your wife has had problems; your best friend has had problems; your parents have had problems; everyone who has participated in the human experience has had problems. And not everyone is thinking about you all the time.

Everyone has their own lives that they are trying to make work, Student. You aren't special!

But if you are to change the way you think—and I don't think you can, but if somehow it slowly happens—your motives about love will have to be "by pureness, by knowledge, by longsuffering, by kindness, by the Holy Ghost, by love unfeigned" (2 Corinthians 6:6). Going out and performing kind acts and service for other people, while at the same time hating yourself, means you are actually using people to help you fill the hole inside your soul. You can get free of my substances all you want, but a drunken horse thief who got sober still remains a horse thief until he fixes the holes in his character and stops stealing horses.

But Student, how do you plan to love your neighbor when you care so much about what your neighbor thinks of you? You care so much about what people think that it's actually selfish on your part. If they don't act like they care about what you are saying or aren't as interested as you might think they should be, you get worried about if they like you. This is your ego, Student. Again, they have their own worries, and not everybody has to be validating your comments or behavior. Remember, you aren't that special.

I don't mind these thoughts and behaviors; the reason I bring them to your attention is to show you how impossible it's going to be to change. To truly love yourself and others means to "love the Lord thy God with all thy heart, and with all thy soul, and with all thy mind" (Matthew 22:37). Maybe there is a reason that the first great commandment is to love God.

Your Fake Friend,
The Devil

LETTER 40
COMPETE FOR INNOCENCE

Dear Student,

Isn't it interesting how far away you have gotten from your childlike self? You used to be physically active and free inside your mind, and now you are plagued with character defects that actually make up who you are today. As a kid, you were "submissive, meek, humble, patient, [and] full of love" (Mosiah 3:19). But as a drug-addicted adult, you are impatient and full of insecurities, doubt, and fear, and you are consumed by the "natural man" (Mosiah 3:19). You can't deal with any downtime, and the monotony inside the sober life seems to be too much.

However, I see you wrestling with the idea of trying to go back to being your childlike self who was "willing to submit to all things which the Lord seeth fit to inflict upon [you], even as a child doth submit to his father" (Mosiah 3:19). The Holy Spirit has always been inside you, Student. It's just that you have buried him for a number of years now. I fear that if you keep competing with your thoughts and abstaining from my team of substances, the Holy Spirit will find a place inside your soul to live.

God talks often about becoming this new creature in Christ. He wants you to "become as little children, and believe that salvation was, and is, and is to come, in and through the atoning blood of Christ" (Mosiah 3:18). But isn't it interesting how he allows you to pick up the world's shiny objects as a learning experience? God would have you look at all adversity as a way to get better, not bitter. He even allowed you to get addicted to drugs, hoping you would use His system of health to find your way back to becoming a child again. He claims that as you fight your way out of the world and finally get clean, you'll be of great benefit to mankind because of the competency you will have developed from having the opportunity to live two lives. Now you'll be able to help other humans who have been blinded by those same shiny objects that blinded you. Interesting!

Student, it almost sounds as if you are starting to believe that your purpose here in mortality is to "taste the bitter, that [you] may know to prize the good" (Moses 6:55; see also D&C 29:39; 2 Nephi 2:1–2, 11); that you are actually being given the opportunity to take part in a great learning experience inside the great school of life; and that your addiction might become a way for you to inspire others to change their lives by "[teaching] one another the doctrine of the kingdom" (D&C 88:77). But again, the only way for you to get in the position to inspire others is to first change your own life in a big way. No more being impatient, no more being loud and vulgar, and no more taking yourself out of reality. This new character change will be a life-long effort to quit. You'll have to quit being negative. You'll have to quit being resentful and hateful. You'll have to quit trying to control everything.

Student, we have talked about all of this before, but I feel that it's necessary to keep reiterating these same penetrating truths. Changing character defects that have been a part of you for many years is no easy feat. You'll be waking up early every morning to "meditate upon these things" (1 Timothy 4:15). You'll be reading, writing, and studying "the doctrine of Christ" (2 John 1:9). You'll be listening to audiobooks and going on walks to "ponder the path of life" (Proverbs 5:6). You'll be running sprints, jogging, hiking, and training in a gym. You'll be going to meetings and sharing. Student, doesn't this all sound exhausting? I'm here to tell you now that this is the only way you'll be able to change your character. You'll have to work as hard as you've ever worked in your life—even blood, sweat, and tears, my friend.

But Student, this is not all. Throughout this process, you're going to have to learn to "suffer with patience these afflictions which shall come upon [you]" (Alma 31:31). Every day in the sober life is filled with high-adventure experiences that will change your plans. You love routine, Student! And things will pop up unexpectedly in the sober life that you'll have to make adjustments for, and I'm not sure you can do this without taking a pill. Most days, you let any little hiccup cause you to have a bad day, but it has been okay in the past because you've had a pill to help you through it. Now, this sober you means walking through daily change while carrying a positive attitude and adapting to any adverse situation by carrying the hope that you "can do all things through Christ which strengtheneth [you]" (Philippians 4:13).

Student, every day, you are going to run into opportunities to say "I told you so," get revenge on someone for how they treated you, or practice what you would say to certain people when they embarrassed you in public or cut you off in traffic. I've already seen you rehearse how you are going to tell someone off. You even seem to find joy in practicing such talk because it offers you a feeling of pride and control. However, such talk and confrontation will not work if you plan to capture sobriety. The stormy brain must turn into a brain of serenity, if you catch my drift, Student. You must be walking around each day carrying "the mind of the Lord, that he may instruct [you]," or you will fail (1 Corinthians 2:16). You must be willing to change your response to many situations that will arise throughout everyday living.

This is why I'm so adamant about you remaining inside my pleasure system of health; this new God-conscious way of life seems nearly impossible for you. You've always been an all-or-nothing personality, so if you can't live this way of life perfect from the get-go, then what's the point in trying, right?

Your Fake Friend,
The Devil

LETTER 41
COMPETE FOR HAPPINESS

Dear Student,

The story goes that Christ took upon Him the dope sickness, depression, withdrawals, "pains and afflictions and temptations of every kind; and this that the word might be fulfilled which saith he will take upon him the pains and the sicknesses of his people" (Alma 7:11). He has already walked through "the valley of the shadow of death" (Psalm 23:4) to take upon Him mankind's misused free agency "to bring about the plan of mercy, to appease the demands of justice, that God might be a perfect, just God, and a merciful God also" (Alma 42:15).

How, exactly, did all of this happen, Student? Do you actually find yourself being able to relate to Christ because of His claim to have felt your pain and anguish? If Christ has felt your pain and anguish, then why doesn't He remove it immediately? I guess it all goes back to Him trying to lead you through those same learning experiences that He had to go through. Christ "descended below all things," right (D&C 88:6)? Therefore, He is the map which you must use to find your way through this life. After all, He is "the light of the world: he that followeth [Him] shall not walk in darkness, but shall have the light of life" (John 8:12).

These learning experiences that come inside the mortal experience have broken many men, Student. To have the competency to work for Christ in the hereafter is the hope for many, but why can't the current life experience be enjoyed to a full measure? Christ is claiming that life is enjoyed to the fullest inside the pain, stress, sadness, and adversities that come inside the mortal experience. But there are many medications to help you coast through life, so pain doesn't have to be felt. Nowadays, I see you self-medicating with exercise and good nutrition practices in an effort to combat your depression, anxiety, and cravings. But Student, there are medications that can help you with your mind struggles. Then you won't have to be a slave to exercising and eating healthy. You have quit drugs and alcohol, and now you are trying to quit food. Student, what's happening to you?

Your Fake Friend,
The Devil

UNIT 10

SELFLESS

Selflessness is the antidote to stress.

LETTER 42
LESS SELF-PITY

Dear Student,

How do you plan to handle your selfish behavior? So far, I'm not impressed. Your selfishness is what has made it easy for me to keep you tangled in my web of substances. For your entire life, Student, you have been selfish enough to even consider yourself more valuable than most. You've always been able to get your way without even realizing that you put others behind you. You've even "broken the [heart] of your tender [wife], and lost the confidence of your children, because of your bad [example] before them" (Jacob 2:35). Now you are climbing the age ladder, and this selfishness has been with you for a lifetime. Good luck trying to become selfless when you have sought to be worshipped. Remember, it is pride that "goeth before . . . a fall" (Proverbs 16:18).

I've heard you praying to God for help with your selfishness and anger in an attempt to "not [be so] easily provoked" (1 Corinthians 13:5). But Student, you reek of selfishness and greed, while the selfless disciples of Christ "seeketh not [their] own" (1 Corinthians 13:5). And you have never denied yourself worldly pleasures, while the selfless disciples of Christ seek to bridle all their passions (see Alma 38:12).

God is trying to get you to grow into a Christlike person, and the only way He can help you capture the constant companionship of the Holy Ghost is by teaching you how to overcome selfishness. God wants you to love your neighbor, which hasn't been you, Student. The only thing you've been in love with is my worldly substances and self-pity. You've had a "mind hardened in pride" (Daniel 5:20). Self-pity is the opposite of selfishness, and the man who is full of self-pity is actually the most selfish of all—even though he thinks that his life is harder than everyone else's. He mopes around, hoping everyone feels sorry for him so that he can capture the good feelings that arise from feeling indifferent to others. This is you to a T, isn't it, Student? You've moped around in front of your wife and kids for years now.

God would have you love Him, and in doing so, you will be released from your egocentric self. But let's be honest: You love "the praise of men more than the praise of God" (John 12:42–43). If you truly loved God, it would be hard to love my lifestyle, Student. But the self-centered person inside you will not die easily. Capturing the "mind of Christ" (1 Corinthians 2:16) will be a lifelong effort of competing with the "natural man" (1 Corinthians 2:14) inside you.

The constant role play in your mind will have to die, yet somehow you find joy in practicing what you would say to others. When someone gives you the hard advice or snubs you, you like practicing how you would tell them off or why your ideas are better than theirs. If you think about it, you spend the majority of your day thinking about how you can control other people to get what you want. From one person to another you go, scheming up scenarios inside your mind on how you would respond to different interactions with these people. What a waste of time this is, Student. What a horrible form of selfishness this has become for you. And the sad thing is you seem to enjoy it, yet you hate it at the same time. What are you to do about this?

The natural man inside you says that you are special and better than everyone else. You even pit your will against God's will by "[seeking] [your] own, not the things which are Jesus Christ's" (Philippians 2:21). Therefore, your will is always in direct competition with God's will, which is why your desires, appetites, and passions are always getting the best of you (see Alma 38:12).

I am very competitive as well, Student, which is why, in the premortal council, my plan was in direct competition with God's plan (see Moses 4:1–3). I wanted all of the glory, Student! And it was my competitive desire to dethrone God and demolish free agency (see D&C 29:36; D&C 76:28).

I love how the natural man inside you eats and drinks alcohol in abundance, takes pills and smokes Weed, and thinks that his routine and schedule are the only routine and schedule that matter. And when anything tries to mess with his pleasure routine, a great manipulation tactic takes shape so that the schedule and routine can mold to his expectations. Your natural man always gets his way, Student.

Therefore, praying for your enemies and those who are spiritually sick must become a consistent practice if you are to escape the prison in your head. No more practicing what you would say or how you would react if you saw such people in public. With this new God mindset, you must be willing to forgive, forget, and even serve. God wants you thinking less of yourself and more about how you can help others to grow. He wants you to turn the other cheek, Student (see Matthew 5:39). And for those people who are talking falsely behind your back, you must pray for them instead of retaliating with harsh words or physical force. Basically, Student, you have to become a pushover who is weak. Is it "the meek [who] shall inherit the earth" (Psalm 37:11)? Or is it the weak? You are weak, Student!

Oftentimes, you feel as if people are plotting against you or saying stuff behind your back. I love how you are so self-centered, Student. Don't you think that most people have better things to think about than just you? People have their own problems and egos to deal with, and they are probably wondering if you or someone else is plotting against them in the same way. What a twist I have all of you humans in; it's almost comical. You all think that you are so important that everyone should be thinking about you, when in reality, everyone is just thinking about themselves. After all, "only by pride cometh contention" (Proverbs 13:10).

This is a selfish world, Student, and if you think about it, standing out amongst your peers isn't that hard to do if you would just be less selfish. But then, after you found yourself being less selfish, you would probably be proud of yourself for doing so. You can't get away from selfishness, Student. You don't have the "humbleness of mind" to change, so quit trying my friend (Colossians 3:12).

Your Fake Friend,

The Devil

LETTER 43
LESS HARMS

Dear Student,

It's interesting how you're starting to believe that you need to have a relationship with God and other people in order to find happiness in this life. For your entire life, Student, you have been self-centered, to the point of actually using people so that all things might swing in your direction. In your addiction, you used everybody so you could experience pleasure and escape. You lied to your wife and spent money, you manipulated your parents, and you cut ties with good friends except when you needed something from them. You've been self-centered for a very long time now. What's your plan for fixing these relationships and harms?

God would have you "bridle all your passions, that ye may be filled with love" (Alma 38:12). He even asks you to make amends to these people by saying you are sorry and showing them that you have changed your life. I would say that this is a risky confession because many people aren't in the business of forgiving. You've been written off by many people—what makes you think they will accept an apology from you, Student?

Do you really want to go back down this road of action? First, it was your resentments and fears that were taking up space in your mind, and now you are circling back to harms because you think that if you don't fix these harms, then you won't fix your addiction. Do you feel guilty, Student, for the harm you have caused others?

This is an interesting philosophy: You think that if you make a list of all the people that you harmed and become willing to make amends, you might feel less guilty for the harms you have caused others. What about your wife and children, Student? Think about all the harm you did to your wife over the years. While you were off hiding behind my substances, she was facing stress head-on. And what about your kids?

Those times when you would leave to go pick up pills and then lie about where you had been. Or even the times when you would take your kids with you to meet your drug dealer, even putting their lives at risk by driving high with them in the car. This is hard news to face, Student. Again, I ask you: Do you really want to go back down this road?

You see, it doesn't feel good to bring such memories back into the light now, does it? Why not just forget them, Student? Apologizing for the way you've acted over the years seems like a waste of time. This order of doing things will only lead you to feel like something is wrong with you. Aren't you interested in being recovered? God would have you believe that He "came into the world not to call the righteous but sinners to repentance" (Moroni 8:8); and that "though your sins be as scarlet, they shall be as white as snow; though they be red like crimson, they shall be as wool" (Isaiah 1:18). He also promised, "he who has repented of his sins, the same is forgiven, and I, the Lord, remember them no more" (D&C 58:42).

So, the question remains, Student: Is repentance necessary in order for one to fully recover? Must you have this "godly sorrow," which "worketh repentance to salvation" (2 Corinthians 7:10)? I would rather have you believe that nothing has ever been wrong with you in the first place. Nothing's wrong with you, Student. You don't need to turn your will and life over to a higher power. By doing so, you will constantly be reminding yourself that something is wrong with you. Nothing is wrong with you! You don't need God! And you don't need to fix your harms; you are able to move on without guilt anyway. Nothing is wrong with you, Student!

This idea that your past harms will block you from God seems silly. In order to truly recover, one must move on, correct? So just move on and forget about the people you have harmed. I wonder if they care to hear from you, anyway? I guess there is some truth behind patching up old relationships that once were meaningful. These beautiful conversations that God hopes for you to experience offer growth, but not without consequence. Tears may flow, and old emotions may come forth that could cause stress to both parties. You don't want to bother others with such emotions, do you?

If I'm being honest, Student, the last thing I want to see is you repairing old relationships and fixing any harms you've done. If you do these things, you will become more like Christ and less like me. Repentance does mean more freedom and peace, but again, with more knowledge comes responsibility, which will lead you to being accountable for the way that you act down the road. This new way of life that you are seeking after doesn't come without consequences, Student.

Keep all of this in mind as you continue to try and "exercise your faith unto repentance" (Alma 34:17).

Your Fake Friend,
The Devil

LETTER 44
LESS NATURAL MAN

Dear Student,

New attributes are being added to your character. I've been tempting, but you've been competing with my temptations and making correct choices that are in line with the lifestyle of Christ. I've been trying to irritate you, though gentleness and passiveness seem to be your reaction. And even though you have many personal problems, your service to others continues. What's happening to the compulsive and impatient character I once knew?

Christ hopes that your natural man dies so that the man of Christ can come forth and become "a saint through the atonement of Christ the Lord" (Mosiah 3:19). But isn't it interesting how He asks you to walk through the shadows of adversity before capturing this new man of Christ; and that "whosoever shall put their trust in God shall be supported in their trials, and their troubles, and their afflictions, and shall be lifted up at the last day" (Alma 36:3)? He asks you to walk by faith into your own personal classrooms to learn through adversity and trial. He asks you to trust in His process without totally knowing if His process is real by carrying a "hope for things which are not seen, which are true" (Alma 32:21). He says that He will bless you, but that "it is by obedience to that law upon which it is predicated" and that such blessings and answers to prayers will be on His timetable and not yours (D&C 130:20–21). He even promised, "if ye will have faith in me ye shall have power to do whatsoever thing is expedient in me" (Moroni 7:33).

But Student, can't you see how much more valuable of a system mine can be in your life? I promise the immediate reward without having to wait. If you want something, I can give it to you now, Student. My systems of immediate pleasure can also improve your character because fast, euphoric thinking is what my substances can offer. And when such euphoria enters your system, your character and way of communicating become heightened to levels that God's system cannot offer. After all, pleasure is what gives meaning to life, Student. God even says, "he that loveth pleasure shall be a poor man: he that loveth wine and oil shall not be rich" (Proverbs 21:17). But many of the rich are addicted to pleasure, Student. I guess it all depends on what you mean by rich. Rich spiritually? Or rich in the ways of the world? Which one is better, Student? I think you know the answer.

But why would God want you to live daily with "a thorn in the flesh" (2 Corinthians 12:7)? Is it true that you are actually trying to "take pleasure in infirmities, in reproaches, in necessities, in persecutions, in distresses for Christ's sake" (2 Corinthians 12:10)? This meek personality that you seek after means a less impulsive personality that becomes a better platform for learning to take place. If pride, arrogance, and ego make up your personality, then learning and growth stand at a halt. It was Christ who said, "Take my yoke upon you, and learn of me; for I am meek and lowly in heart: and ye shall find rest unto your souls" (Matthew 11:29).

With meekness, you become willing to hear the truth without it offending you. But aren't you worried about becoming a weak pushover, Student? The mindset of letting go and putting your "trust in the true and living God" means that you are fearful and weak (Alma 5:13). The strong only survive and thrive by trying to control all persons, places, and things. But if you let go and love God, then God will be in control and not you, which means that the show won't be under your control anymore. Why, then, would you want to give up control and succumb to this meek type of personality that you have been searching after?

God's plan calls for you to live with hard situations that you might not be able to change; He asks you to endure to the end without becoming mad or bitter about the hard times that life has presented to you. This addiction disease that you've come to obtain is hard, and if I were you, I would keep feeling sorry for myself—after all, you are special and different from everyone else.

This addiction is a long-term challenge that isn't going to go away, Student. It's not like the challenge of the moment that is sure to pass at some point. This addiction disease is going to be a life-long battle in which service to others is the only cure. The remedy for sad thinking is engulfing yourself in the service of others, because doing so will lead to selflessness. And when one is selfless, it frees up the mind to enjoy the moment. Christ even taught, "If any man will come after me, let him deny himself, and take up his cross, and follow me" (Matthew 16:24). But Student, it's inside the selfish mind that worry and resentment can develop until irritation becomes so bad that the only option becomes to escape through my team of substances.

But these are all ideas and concepts that you are well aware of, and the reason for me bringing them to your attention is to discourage you from the long journey ahead.

It's all so complicated, so why not just take my easy way of escape?

Your Fake Friend,
The Devil

LETTER 45

LESS EGO

Dear Student,

I see you striving to act more "meek and lowly in heart" so that your spiritual condition can remain high in an effort to limit your impulsive and destructive behavior (Matthew 11:29). I guess you have found out the truth behind being kind and generous to others and its relationship to feeling at peace inside your mind. Your scriptures even say, "Let nothing be done through strife or vainglory; but in lowliness of mind let each esteem other better than themselves" (Philippians 2:3).

But Student, being loud and impulsive means being funny and unique. Again, you are unique, Student. It would be ordinary for you to be more humble with your views on life. Your views on life are special and make up who you are. Your views on life are why people like you. You don't need to let others say what you already know to be true. The limelight must always come back to you because it's your point of view that matters the most. And anyway, you are the master communicator and concept creator, which means those with whom you are conversing actually want to hear from you instead of them being heard by you.

Why try to fight the feelings of being offended, Student? You've made no mistakes, so why bother admitting that you were wrong? People aren't allowed to point out your faults without you pointing out their faults as well. You execute at a higher level than most, which means you have learned enough and don't need corrective counsel. What these people are really saying is that you are dumb and aren't competent enough to complete the task at hand. It's totally normal to practice what you are going to say to these people in a resentful tone, because your resentments are completely justified. You are better and smarter than them, so why should you have to take hard counsel from them?

There is nothing wrong with your ego, Student. It's impossible to "be humble, . . . submissive and gentle; easy to be entreated; [and] full of patience and long-suffering; being temperate in all things" (Alma 7:23). Your ego is why you are so competitive. If you keep trying to get rid of your ego, you'll lose your competitive edge over everyone and everything. You'll start allowing others to share in the limelight, and your view on life will become more settled and ordinary. Now, when you get some bad news, you'll take it in humble stride instead of reacting negatively and impulsively.

I guess if you are interested in removing all pleasure and fun from your life, then keep this sort of thought process going.

Your Fake Friend,

The Devil

UNIT 11

SERVICE

Service eliminates the brain storm.

LETTER 46
SERVING OTHERS

Dear Student,

It's quite obvious that something is happening to you. Inside your heart and mind, there seems to be a new charity growing, even "the pure love of Christ" (Moroni 7:47). But this idea to quit your day job to start an addiction recovery program seems absurd, Student. What will you do about insurance and money for your family? I know you can feel the still, small voice pushing you towards this direction, but think how crazy that all sounds. You haven't been on the foundation of Christ for that long, so what makes you think that you'll stay on it for the duration of your life?

This idea might just be a part of your compulsive personality, which, remember, you are trying to get rid of anyway. The economy is at an all-time low, and for you to pull this off would be nothing short of a miracle. Again, what are you going to do about money? God would have you believe that "when ye are in the service of your fellow beings ye are only in the service of your God" (Mosiah 2:17). He wants you to believe that this is your true calling in life and that everything that's happened up to this point was necessary in order for you to find your calling. But Student, think how ridiculous this all sounds. Do you honestly think that if you participate in God's service system that you cannot fail?

A life in the service of others really means a life thinking less about yourself. But to think that making your life's work one of helping people to change their lives is a tall order. There isn't much money and financial security if you do choose to go this direction. Yes, you might feel all warm and fuzzy, but that won't stop you from having to foreclose on your home, which is sure to happen. You'll have to skip car payments and max out your credit cards, which means your credit score will fall desperately low.

But God keeps telling you to "put your trust in him, and serve him with all diligence of mind, [and] if ye do this, he will, according to his own will and pleasure, deliver you out of bondage" (Mosiah 7:33). Then you will experience peace and stability. Yes, a life built on the foundation of Christ "is a sure foundation, a foundation whereon if men build they cannot fall" (Helaman 5:12). But such a foundation cannot protect you against adversity, stress, and even heartache.

Growing in this direction requires fortitude and diligence because, if you're going to make an impact in the lives of other people, you'll have to continue to fix your own life, Student. No one finds inspiration from the one who hasn't been through something hard. If you choose to take this calling, then you can plan on a lot of shadow work inside the "great mist of darkness," my friend (1 Nephi 8:23). I will be tempting you stronger than ever before because now, you are my enemy. When you were on my side, you weren't a threat, Student. But now you are a threat to my entire operation by how you are trying to steer my other drifting students who have "wandered off and [are] lost" back towards the foundation of Christ, which I obviously cannot let happen (1 Nephi 8:23).

So go ahead and press forward if you dare, but just keep in mind that I'll be waiting to catch you when you fall from the "strait and narrow path" to again "[wander] in strange roads" (1 Nephi 8:20, 32). The still, small voice keeps whispering, and you keep listening, which I'll have to go ahead and do something about, won't I?

Be ready for the brain storm, Student.

Your Fake Friend,

The Devil

LETTER 47
SERVING CHRIST

Dear Student,

Every day, you are "[talking] of Christ, [rejoicing] in Christ, [and preaching] of Christ," almost as a way to keep your spiritual condition high, which is obviously selfish on your part (2 Nephi 25:26). Do you really think that by doing so, you are helping others to come unto Christ as well? Even your wife and kids, Student? What happens when you become fanatical and over the top, to the point that those around you get tired of your preaching, teaching, and coaching? Nobody likes the try-hard, Student, especially nowadays. You just may change your life in such a massive way that judgment towards others becomes the next step.

Do you really think that faith accompanies work, Student? Doesn't the adage "Let go and let God" mean you do nothing at all and rely on God entirely? Yet God is always asking you to be "anxiously engaged in a good cause, . . . [bringing] to pass much righteousness" (D&C 58:27) so you can become a master teacher, coach, and missionary to those other students who have "wandered off and [are] lost" (1 Nephi 8:23) and likewise need the help of Jesus Christ.

Apparently, there is a great "increase in learning" to be had when working with others to help them overcome their addictions, which in turn helps you to overcome your addictions (Proverbs 9:9). This idea of loving your neighbor really means growing towards Christ and His peaceful way of life, while at the same time engaging in beautiful conversations that lead to lifelong friendships.

But isn't being in the service of others, especially those who struggle with drug and alcohol addiction, quite burdensome? As you grow your character upwards, their dark character will bring you down quickly with all of their negativity and self-pity. Why not just move on and enjoy your new, hopeful character? Unless, of course, you think that the driving force behind your new character stems from you being in their service. But if you are in their service with such improper motives, wouldn't your service to them be selfish anyway? Student, once again, this all seems to be so confusing. The roadblocks to gaining access to the Atonement of Jesus Christ are many, so why keep trying?

If you are serious about such discipleship, then it will mean putting pressure on a healthy way of life over a long period of time. You will have to make a series of correct choices over the long haul, and when you fall off this straight and narrow path, the only way back on it is through repentance—because "strait is the gate, and narrow is the way, which leadeth unto life, and few there be that find it" (Matthew 7:14).

Basically, Student, you'll have to go through the long process of asking God for forgiveness with a "broken heart and a contrite spirit" and then aligning your way of life with Jesus Christ (3 Nephi 12:19). You'll have to remain obedient to the commandments because "by small and simple things are great things brought to pass" (Alma 37:6). However, this is no small order in this world full of pleasure and fast results.

> Wherefore, ye must press forward with a steadfastness in Christ, having a perfect brightness of hope, and a love of God and of all men. Wherefore, if ye shall press forward, feasting upon the word of Christ, and endure to the end, behold, thus saith the Father: Ye shall have eternal life. (2 Nephi 31:20)

A life of trying is what God is asking of you, Student. Again, He has such high expectations in a world full of so much pleasure. I'm only asking you to "eat, drink, and be merry, for tomorrow [you] die," so why not live it up to the fullest now (2 Nephi 28:7)?

Your Fake Friend,

The Devil

LETTER 48
SERVING SUFFERING

Dear Student,

During this new journey of service, you seem to be experiencing sorrow and suffering. Your soul is being stretched, and your "over anxiety" about money and holding on to your possessions is making it so you can't work with people to the best of your ability (Jacob 4:18). You are constantly worried if you're going to make it financially, and losing your house is right around the corner. But remember, Student, "God hath not given [you] the spirit of fear; but of power, and of love, and of a sound mind" (2 Timothy 1:7). However, what is your wife going to think? She's probably going to think that you aren't man enough to provide for her and the kids. I hate to say it, Student, but I told you so.

And yes, you are helping people, I'll give you that, but at what cost? All you do is work, and when you come home at night you go directly to your computer while your wife manages the kids, puts them to bed, and then goes to sleep. The two of you barely talk and don't even sleep in the same bed anymore; your new addiction is working, Student. You are addicted to finding success, so what's the difference from when you were addicted to pills?

But you know what would help your stress, Student? Opiates would help your stress. Isn't it hard to work with all of these addicted students and not go back to being addicted yourself? You are financially strapped! You are losing your house! You've put your family at risk! I hope it was worth helping others yet not being able to help your own family.

Go ahead and relapse on pills! I mean, what do you really have to lose at this point anyway? You're probably going to lose your business, your house, and possibly your wife. Your life is pathetic. But keep chasing this pipe dream of changing the world. And trust me, you aren't making much of an impact anyway. Go ahead and quit and become just like everyone else. Go get the nine-to five job and be ordinary. I already told you that you were special and different, but you kept fighting against those thoughts as you sought to become more humble and meek. Now I'm telling you to go ahead and be ordinary. Shut the doors to your business and go back to being comfortable. You're weak! And anyway, "he that loveth pleasure shall be a poor man" (Proverbs 21:17). And we both know that you love pleasure.

Your Fake Friend,
The Devil

LETTER 49
SERVING RESENTMENTS

Dear Student,

To serve is to love, right? But Student, "no servant can serve two masters: for either he will hate the one, and love the other; or else he will hold to the one, and despise the other. Ye cannot serve God and mammon" (Luke 16:13). Yet service is so demanding. It's demanded that you focus on others instead of your wife and kids. It's demanded that you lose your house. It's demanded that you become selfish from being in the service of others. Student, you should be proud of yourself for how much you have helped people. Remember, you have a gift and are special.

Aren't you resentful at all of this? Aren't you mad for choosing to take on this calling from God? Now your family goes without, while you try and offer drug addicts and alcoholics a new way of life. Your wife and kids are suffering! Student, you've even lost your house and have had to move your family into an apartment. I must ask again: What were you thinking when you decided to take this leap of faith?

Well, there is the belief that if you serve Him, then eventually your life will be built upon "a foundation whereon if men build they cannot fall" (Helaman 5:12). But you are failing by letting your wife and kids down by losing your house and having to move them into an apartment. Aren't you embarrassed? You claim to have never gone without, yet you are going without, Student. God says that upon this foundation you cannot fall, but you are falling.

Even I cannot deny that your small sacrifices have helped numerous people, which is admirable. But how do you plan to keep answering your phone and serving a population that has very little resources? How do you plan to provide for your family long-term? You are helping the drug addict but letting your family down at the same time. Sometimes, I get the feeling that your work is far more important than your family, which seems selfish. Here you are trying to serve while at the same time finding yourself more and more selfish around the ones you love. Even your wife seems detached because you are distancing yourself from her while you place such a high emphasis on the uniqueness of your work.

My biggest concern is the mindset that your life's calling is to serve and coach those other struggling students who have the same disease as you; that you "may be an instrument in the hands of God to bring some soul to repentance" (Alma 29:9). This is a powerful mindset that can give one purpose, I guess. However, you also think that your mistakes inside the School of Addiction were actually learning experiences so you could help others. You think that your tough travel through the school's shadows has given you a unique opportunity and ability to serve others. Wow! This is impressive doctrine, but once again, there is no tangible evidence to support that God is trying to school you on how to help yourself and others.

Is God providing you and your family with the necessary means to stay afloat during these early stages of working with people? Are you still in tune with the still, small voice that whispers insight and peace into your soul concerning the future (see 1 Kings 19:12)? Are you motivated to keep all this up by having faith that, if you build your life on the foundation of Christ, then you cannot fall?

Again, what comforting insight. But is it real? It almost sounds selfish to think that God is supporting you in such a massive way when He has billions upon billions of other children to support as well, or that "the very hairs of your head are all numbered" (Matthew 10:30). Let's be honest: You are just a small speck in a selfish world. But maybe it's true that whatever you think about you bring about. Maybe that's what faith is anyway, Student. If you think about God enough and try and align your way of life with His, then your hopes and dreams will come to pass. However, "in process of time" means you must have patience (Moses 7:21).

Your Fake Friend,
The Devil

LETTER 50
SERVING TRYING

Dear Student,

It seems you have chosen to take part in a life of trying, but I'm not worried. "Wherefore, if ye have sought to do wickedly in the days of your probation, then ye are found unclean before the judgment-seat of God; and no unclean thing can dwell with God" (1 Nephi 10:21). So you see, Student, I have plenty of time to convince you that the "strait and narrow path which leads to eternal life" isn't full of high-adventure experiences (2 Nephi 31:18). Eventually, boredom, monotony, and the stresses of life will cause you to crumble just like in times past, and you will be back on my team once again.

I always win, Student! I'm winning the war during this mortal experience, yet I get the feeling that God believes He has the actual upper hand. Christ even "offereth himself a sacrifice for sin, to answer the ends of the law, unto all those who have a broken heart and a contrite spirit" (2 Nephi 2:7). Therefore, His great sacrifice for mankind requires that they repent, and only then can mercy "appease the demands of justice" (Alma 42:15).

In the current time period, people have become "lovers of their own selves" (2 Timothy 3:2), to which "the love of many shall wax cold" (Matthew 24:12), making it hard for the "humble followers of Christ" (2 Nephi 28:14) to gain any momentum on this "strait and narrow path" (2 Nephi 31:18).

God has counseled you to make serving others a part of your life. And you've come to believe that it's your life's calling to use your God-given talents to help those other students who are struggling to find their way to Jesus Christ.

It's interesting how you've come to grips with your basic role as a father. You now see that the greatest service opportunities actually happen inside your family as you stay sober. But again, I still see you taking your professional life of working with others home, and you become selfish again towards your family. Why does God set you up to fail in such a way, Student? He puts all this pressure on you to serve your clients, but you keep falling short inside your home. Again, the yoke of Christ is a symbol of discipleship, yet it is also a heavy burden since it requires you to always be competing with yourself. You used to never carry the awareness of trying to be patient and selfless inside your home; now, since coming unto Christ, you are full of this new awareness, which has actually become burdensome.

God would have you live His lifestyle and then share what you have learned with others so they can experience, for themselves, the healing powers of the Atonement of Jesus Christ. But I would rather have you be engaged in your same manipulation tactics of lying and stealing. I would rather have you away from your family, being selfish instead of selfless. Your wife doesn't like you, Student, and neither do your kids. They've seen your natural man side the most, and that's who they know you to be, Student. They don't understand this new man of Christ that's trying to come forth.

The world at large is selfish, and if you go this selfless route, then you will stand out amongst the crowds and be headed towards the "narrow gate, [to] walk in the strait path which leads to life" (2 Nephi 33:9). To think that serving in this life experience is for learning purposes is absurd. Those beautiful conversations that you seek after while being in the service of your family, friends, and neighbors are what bring you into the present moment to help you escape your head prison. Now, if you are thinking of others, you cannot be in competition with others—unless, of course, your motives aren't as pure as you think.

Round and round we go, Student, with you trying to act like your motives are pure, while I'm trying to show you that nothing is pure. You humans are easily provoked—if you are not trying to improve your character, then you are actually going backwards, and it is at the root of your soul that selfishness lies. You all think of yourselves the most, which makes this game easy for me. If I can keep you selfish, then I can keep you sick.

Your Fake Friend,
The Devil

THE PRIDE CYCLE

Things are going good. You're comfortable.

LETTER 51
PRIDE AND POWER

Dear Student,

How are you going to deal with the pride cycle now that you are full of this positive light of Christ? It's always true that individuals who capture power end up becoming "lovers of their own selves, covetous, proud, . . . unthankful, unholy, [and] without natural affection" (2 Timothy 3:2–3).

Student, do you really believe that "there are many called, but few are chosen" and that "the powers of heaven cannot be controlled nor handled only upon the principles of righteousness" (121:34–36)? I've seen you come to grips with the idea that if you live a life in line with the commandments of Christ that you will be blessed. You seem to now be humbled by the word instead of "being compelled to be humble" by events that would cause you to be humbled, like your addiction (Alma 32:8–16). Early on, it was your addiction that humbled you to put on the yoke of Christ, but nowadays, you are doing it because you are humbled by having "seen God moving in his majesty and power" (D&C 88:47).

But again, this personality you seek after is impossible to obtain in such a fast and loud world. You're looking for a quiet strength that does not exist, Student. To stay poised and reverent in the world means not only taking the yoke of Christ upon you but also staying open to the possibility that you aren't in control of the game anyway.

The present moment is all that matters, Student. You cannot change the past through worry; you can only do the next right thing. Over time, this series of correct choices will lead to a mindset that is built upon true principles. However, this type of mindset leaves you open to hope and faith, which means you cannot prove that what you hope to happen in your life will happen. You will have to trust God's promises, Student, that if you do "the works of righteousness," you "shall receive [your] reward, even peace in this world, and eternal life in the world to come" (D&C 59:23).

But I would rather have you carrying around the fixed mindset so that you can maintain control of where your life goes. This means to go ahead and turn your life over to the care of God, but don't do anything at all to bring about change in your life. God will handle it if He's there, so don't worry about competing with the "natural man" inside you (Mosiah 3:19).

It's interesting how your conscience has developed. In the past, nothing bothered you, yet today, your conscious mind tells you to "Let go and let God." But if you do that, who is to take control of your emotions? Aren't you tired of feeling bad for the way you've acted in your past now that you have an active conscience telling you the details between right and wrong? Who is to say that my ways are wrong and that God's ways are right? Gravity is a true principle that cannot change. Do God's principles ever change? Or are they the "same yesterday, today, and forever" (Mormon 9:9)?

The Holy Spirit, in "a still small voice," promotes the meek, humble, temperate personality so that God can guide you as a missionary coach (1 Kings 19:11–12). But the leader inside you, Student, is "easily provoked" towards anger, pride, and jealousy (1 Corinthians 13:5). If you take on this leadership role and become a role model, how can you escape your feelings of inadequacy as many of your students grow beyond you? And they will grow beyond you, so how do you plan to remain at the top when so many will be coming after your light?

But to keep pushing forward in your learning from books and life experience is valuable, I guess. Most great leaders are readers, right? Well, the leaders who remain meek become great leaders because the meek mindset is actually the growth mindset. Those with such a mindset aren't as hardened when they read principles of truth, because now those same principles can take root and blossom into something real and lasting. But again, what is truth anyway, Student?

Is being meek, lowly, and humble a true way to live your life? Would anybody ever say that to be more meek would be a bad thing? But again, the meek personality can also be a form of weakness. Often, the one who is lowly will let others have the limelight, which means they become pushovers who aren't great leaders. In your business dealings, you will have to be firm and bold, and you'll have to give hard advice to other struggling students by "reproving betimes with sharpness, when moved upon by the Holy Ghost; and then showing forth afterwards an increase of love toward him whom thou hast reproved, lest he esteem thee to be his enemy" (D&C 121:43). Can you be this type of person if you are meek and lowly? After all, to be meek means to be weak, Student.

There is talk of great leaders possessing "humbleness of mind" (Colossians 3:12). But how are you going to handle when you're not the only one making decisions? Your insecurities about remaining at the top won't "let thy . . . bowels be full of charity towards all men," nor will they allow for "virtue [to] garnish thy thoughts unceasingly" (D&C 121:45).

Regardless if you capture this new growth mindset that is linked to the lowly personality, firm roadblocks will still be placed in your way to create anger and frustration. If I can keep you mad, resentful, and fearful, then nothing will change in your life. Yes, the meek personality will help you to grow at an accelerated rate, because relapse will become less frequent, and you will be far more open to hearing the truth when it raises its ugly head. Even still, I have further plans for you, Student.

Your Fake Friend,

The Devil

LETTER 52
PRIDEFUL BLESSINGS

Dear Student,

What is this incessant talk of miracles and blessings? Yes, of course, if one participates in a healthy lifestyle, it does mean they are blessed. But does that mean that God blesses you because of your work at changing from an unhealthy way of life to a healthy one? If you participate in a healthy lifestyle, then healthy results are what follow. And if you participate in an unhealthy way of life, then unhealthy results are what follow. Fair enough, Student! But who's to say that God is blessing you because of your decision to show diligence to a healthy way of life? Who's to say that all people aren't blessed if they just participate in health and don't worry about gaining a relationship with God?

Your life has improved dramatically, and you give all the credit to God and Jesus Christ. But why would you need them when you can participate in health on your own? You made these changes on your own, Student, so why be held accountable by a higher power who is going to do nothing more than make you feel bad about yourself for the way you act? The tale of life is failure, and if you stay in a relationship with God, you'll be engulfed in an apologetic state quite often. And after a while of feeling bad for the way you act, things will start to fall apart in your mind.

But seeing the hand of God in your life will again take work, Student. It will be tough for you to recognize the blessings of the Almighty if you are engulfed in sin. And anyway, my ways of directing your attention elsewhere will cause you to forget about these blessings, which will essentially lead you to justify why they happened in the first place. They happen out of chance, Student! They happen because what you think about you bring about. Positive thinking breeds positive results, and vice versa. So let's not pretend that this has anything to do with God and Jesus Christ. Blessings are offered to the diligent because they showed persistence and dedication to a true system. Is God's system of health true? Well, I can't say that it's not, but the question remains: Would you have gotten to where you are now without God?

Student, how do you know if the course of life that you are currently on is the right one? Is it because ever since you turned your life over to the care of God you've never gone without? Is it because you now feel an overwhelming sense of peace and comfort? Is it because you now have purposeful feelings in regard to your career and way of life?

I don't know what to tell you, Student, other than that the path you are on is far too simple and monotonous. Life isn't that simple, so quit trying to act like you are involved in an inspired process where you have help every step of the way. No such thing exists, because again, the tale of life takes place inside the shadows of adversity. Even God promotes such adversity, but you "can do all things through Christ which strengtheneth [you]," right (Philippians 4:13)? You can capture a great learning experience that leads you closer to him. But I would say that's a silly belief system, because what creator wants his children to suffer? But then again, true fun is linked to challenge, right?

Your Fake Friend,

The Devil

LETTER 53
PRIDE IN TIME

Dear Student,

Yes, you've got some sober time, but it's only a matter of time before you relapse again. The life choices you've made these last years are impressive, and the addiction recovery program you've created has helped a great number of people. God must be proud of you, Student.

But there are other angles I wish to tempt you from. You still struggle with your resentments and fears, and let's be honest, that's all part of your unique personality anyway. I'm not sure those types of thoughts will ever completely go away. And of course, you can keep conditioning yourself to think otherwise, but what a challenging life that's going to be for you.

Just think: For the remainder of your life, you are going to be in competition with your selfish side. You serve others daily, and your family life has come together nicely, yet I still see the competition inside you growing with more intensity. You still find yourself pushing the limits of your ability in an effort to create something that can be of use to the world. You want to create this special platform that other struggling students in the School of Addiction can find purpose in. You hope that these students can find what you found, will be touched by the spirit of charity, and will capture the ability to create art inside the great School of Addiction.

But what is this art you keep speaking of? Is it for students to gain the new ability to coach and persuade people on how to change their lives in the School of Addiction? Is it for them to write books and pitch concepts that are in line with principles of truth? Is it for them to lead students through the 12-step repentance process and on to find a higher power that asks them to compete daily with their natural man? Is it for them to teach students how to create outdoor spiritual experiences, how to eat healthy, and how to lifts weights?

This seems like a unique art form that is asking a lot of your students. And let's be honest: Most people are lazy and won't be willing to participate in such a challenging School of Addiction. Why would they want to participate in this higher order of living when they could go to a school that offers sobriety but doesn't take as much work?

Student, I'm going to tell you one last secret: The reason most people don't get off my substances is that they don't have the willingness, nor the courage, to participate in this higher order of life. The School of Addiction Recovery isn't for the faint of heart, and most of you humans will grow "wearied and faint in your minds" (Hebrews 12:3).

I'm not worried at all about the direction you're going, so don't think you've got me beat. Remember, I've been coaching people for a long time; therefore, the odds are still in my favor. I know how you think, Student. Yes, you have the Holy Spirit as your current guide, which makes it hard for me to pull you back into the shadows, but time will only tell if you have what it takes to "endure to the end, in following the example of the Son of the living God" (2 Nephi 31:16).

Your Fake Friend,
The Devil

LETTER 54
PRIDE TO SOAR

Dear Student,

This seems to be the end of the story, for now. However, you and I both know the story is far from over. You see it all the time in people who change their lives for a great number of years but then fall back into my team of substances. I have no doubt that this will be you and many of your students as well. The peaceful life of Christ is no match for the fast, euphoric life that I offer. This is a life-long battle of trying to keep your spiritual condition high. And if your spirit does not remain healthy, then neither will your mind. Then it will be easy for me to slip back in and persuade you otherwise.

I have to say that I'm impressed with how you've competed against me and my team these past years. We've had to work hard to keep you on our side and, to be honest, we've learned from the battle, which will only make us stronger as we coach other students. You see, you aren't the only one who is learning, Student. We have unlimited pupils to run our experiments on, which gives us an unfair advantage. Your School of Addiction Recovery is limited compared to our dark school of learning. Most people enjoy pleasure; they will always be in search of fast ways to escape the everyday stresses that take place inside the mortal experience. Therefore, my numbers will always remain higher than God's, for I am winning the WAR.

Maybe it was necessary for you to experience my shadowy WAR inside the School of Addiction so you could gain a priceless learning experience from being in a relationship with my team of substances. Maybe it's time for you to SOAR and make an entrance into this higher order of learning inside the School of Addiction Recovery so your life's purpose can be made manifest in helping those other struggling students find recovery in the great School of Addiction.

You should be so proud of yourself, Student. Just keep in mind that none of this may be true. You might be crazy, Student. But then again, you might be a genius as well. Remember, you are special and different from everyone else.

So, I guess this is goodbye for now. Good luck in trying to teach your students how to SOAR. And trust me, I'll be there to catch them when they fall. After all, "pride goeth before destruction, and an haughty spirit before a fall" (Proverbs 16:18).

Your Fake Friend,

The Devil

Made in the USA
San Bernardino, CA
25 June 2020